b) Any two from: e.g. she should use a sharp pencil. / She should draw outlines of the main features. / She should not colour or shade her drawing. / She should label her drawing with straight, uncrossing lines. / She should include the magnification used and a scale. / Her drawing should take up at least half of the space available. / She should keep the parts in proportion. *[2 marks — 1 for each correct answer.]*

c) The image viewed with an electron microscope would be clearer and more detailed than the image viewed with the light microscope *[1 mark]*. This is because electron microscopes have a higher magnification *[1 mark]* and a higher resolution than light microscopes *[1 mark]*.

Pages 5-6 — More Microscopy

Warm-up

1

	÷ 1000 will convert to:	× 1000 will convert to:	in standard form original unit will be:
mm	m	μm	× 10^{-3} m
μm	**mm**	**nm**	× 10^{-6} m
nm	μm	**pm**	× 10^{-9} m
pm	**nm**		× 10^{-12} m

2 Total magnification = **eyepiece lens** magnification × **objective lens** magnification

It doesn't matter which way round you write eyepiece lens and objective lens in the formula.

$$\text{magnification} = \frac{\text{image size}}{\textbf{real size}}$$

1 a) i) Total magnification = eyepiece lens magnification × objective lens magnification
Total magnification = 10 × 100 = × **1000** *[1 mark]*
   ii) 25 μm *[1 mark]*
The height of the cells is about 2 and a half times the length of the scale bar.

b) A *[1 mark]*

2 a) length of cell A in image = 24 mm
magnification = image size ÷ real size
= 24 ÷ 0.012 = × **2000**
[2 marks for correct answer, otherwise 1 mark for length of cell = 24 mm]

b) image size = magnification × real size
400 × 0.012 = **4.8 mm** *[2 marks for correct answer, otherwise 1 mark for 400 × 0.012]*

3 a) real size = image size ÷ magnification
real size = 10 mm ÷ 1000 = 0.01 mm
0.01 mm x 1000 = **10 μm** *[3 marks for correct answer, otherwise 1 mark for 10 ÷ 1000, 1 mark for 0.01 × 1000]*

b) 4 × 10^{-5} = 0.00004 mm
0.00004 mm × 1000 = 0.04 μm
0.04 μm × 1000 = **40 nm** *[3 marks for correct answer, otherwise 1 mark for 0.00004 × 1000, 1 mark for 0.04 × 1000]*

Pages 7-8 — Enzymes

1 a) A catalyst increases the rate of a reaction *[1 mark]*.
b) active site *[1 mark]*
c) It means usually only one type of substrate will fit into the active site of a specific enzyme *[1 mark]*.

2 a) A *[1 mark]*
b) After a certain point, all of the active sites on the enzymes are full *[1 mark]* and increasing substrate concentration does not result in more substrate molecules entering the active sites of enzymes, so the rate of the reaction is not affected *[1 mark]*.

3 At 38 °C enzyme A will be most active as this is its optimum temperature *[1 mark]*. At 60 °C, enzyme A is denatured and will not be active *[1 mark]* because the shape of the active site has changed *[1 mark]*.

4 a) i)

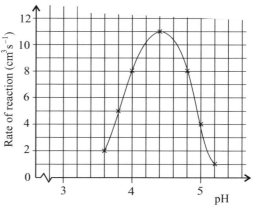

[1 marks for all points correctly plotted, 1 mark for a smooth curve of best fit]
   ii) optimum pH = 4.4 *[1 mark]*
b) The enzyme activity decreases *[1 mark]* because the pH affects the bonds in the enzyme, causing the active site to change shape *[1 mark]* and denaturing the enzyme *[1 mark]*.

Page 9 — More on Enzymes

1 a) pH 6 as this was the pH at which the iodine solution stopped turning blue-black first *[1 mark]*, meaning the starch had been broken down the fastest *[1 mark]*.
b) E.g. the amylase was denatured by the high pH, so the starch was not broken down *[1 mark]*.
c) i) By putting the test tubes in a water bath *[1 mark]*.
   ii) Any two from: e.g. the concentration of starch solution *[1 mark]* / the concentration of amylase *[1 mark]* / the volume of starch and amylase solution added to the iodine / the volume of iodine solution in the wells *[1 mark]*. *[Maximum of 2 marks available]*.
d) E.g. test the solutions more frequently (e.g. every 10 seconds) *[1 mark]*.

Page 10 — Enzymes in Breakdown and Synthesis

1 a) A: carbohydrase *[1 mark]*
B: protein *[1 mark]*
C: amino acids *[1 mark]*
b) Organisms need to be able to break down large molecules into smaller components so that they can be absorbed into the bloodstream and into cells *[1 mark]* to be used for growth and other life processes *[1 mark]*.

2 Orlistat prevents lipase from working so lipids are not broken down *[1 mark]* into fatty acids and glycerol *[1 mark]*. This means lipids are not absorbed into the blood and instead pass through the digestive system and into the faeces *[1 mark]*.

Page 11 — Testing for Biological Molecules

Warm-up
Biuret test — Proteins, Benedict's test — Reducing sugars, Emulsion test — Lipids, Iodine test — Starch

1 a) E.g. add the sample of egg whites to a test tube containing ethanol *[1 mark]*. Shake the tube for about a minute until the egg whites dissolve *[1 mark]*. Pour the solution into water *[1 mark]*. If any lipids are present, they will precipitate out of the liquid and show up as a milky emulsion, if no lipids are present, no milky emulsion will appear *[1 mark]*.
b) Add a few drops of potassium hydroxide to a sample of the egg whites *[1 mark]* and then add some copper(II) sulfate solution *[1 mark]*. If proteins are present, then the solution will turn purple and if not then the solution will be blue *[1 mark]*.

Topic 2

2 a) He should add Benedict's reagent to each of the solutions *[1 mark]*, then heat the test tubes in a water bath that's set to 75 °C *[1 mark]*. He should then look out for the formation of a coloured precipitate and note the colour if one is formed *[1 mark]*.

Glucose is a reducing sugar so the Benedict's test can be used to determine the relative concentrations of glucose in the test tubes.

b)

	Tube 1	Tube 2	Tube 3	Tube 4
substance observed	yellow precipitate	blue solution	red precipitate	green precipitate
glucose concentration (M)	0.1	0	1	0.02

[1 mark]

The higher the concentration of glucose in the solution, the further the colour change goes along the following scale: blue — green — yellow — orange — brick red. If no precipitate forms then there are no reducing sugars in the solution.

Page 12 — Energy in Food

1 a) calorimetry *[1 mark]*
b) temperature change of water = 49.0 °C – 20.0 °C = 29.0 °C
energy content of crisp = 20 × 29 × 4.2 = **2436 J** *[2 marks for correct answer, otherwise 1 mark for temperature change of water = 29.0 °C]*
c) 1890 ÷ 0.56 = **3375 J/g** *[1 mark]*
d) Any one from: e.g. burn each food until it no longer relights / hold each food the same distance away from the boiling tube / ensure that the environmental temperature stays the same throughout the experiment *[1 mark]*.
e) i) 2402 J = 2.402 kJ
2.402 ÷ 0.24 = 10.0083...
10.0083... × 100 = **1000.83 kJ/100 g**
[3 marks for correct answer, otherwise 1 mark for 2.402 kJ and 1 mark for ÷ 0.24]
ii) Some of the energy from burning the food has been transferred to the environment instead of increasing the temperature of the water in her experiment *[1 mark]*.

Pages 13-14 — Diffusion, Osmosis and Active Transport

Warm-up

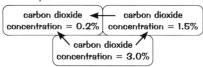

1 a) Diffusion is the net movement *[1 mark]* of particles from an area of higher concentration to an area of lower concentration *[1 mark]*.
b) A *[1 mark]*
2 a) C *[1 mark]*
Remember, osmosis involves the movement of **water** *molecules (so the answer isn't option B or D) across a partially permeable membrane (so the answer isn't option A).*
b) Osmosis is the net movement of water molecules across a partially permeable membrane *[1 mark]* from a region of higher water concentration to a region of lower water concentration / from a region of lower solute concentration to a region of higher solute concentration *[1 mark]*.
3 a) ——————————→ *[1 mark]*
b) ——————————→ *[1 mark]*
c) ←—————————— *[1 mark]*
For this question you need to work out the relative concentration of the molecules on each side of the membrane and read the question carefully to see what process is involved in their movement.

4 a) The epithelial cells have a higher concentration of amino acids than the gut *[1 mark]*, so amino acids have to be moved up their concentration gradient into the epithelial cells *[1 mark]* before they can pass into the bloodstream *[1 mark]*.
b) The structures labelled A are mitochondria *[1 mark]*. These are the site of respiration reactions, which transfer the energy needed for active transport *[1 mark]*.

Page 15 — Investigating Osmosis

1 a) % change in mass = (final mass – initial mass) ÷ initial mass × 100 = (9.3 – 10) ÷ 10 = –0.07 × 100 = **–7%** *[1 mark]*
b) The water concentration was lower inside the potato chips than in the solution in the beaker *[1 mark]*, so the potato chips gained mass as water was drawn into them by osmosis *[1 mark]*.
c)

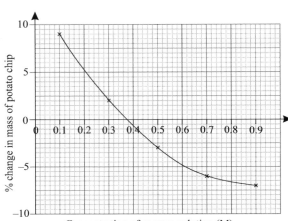

[1 mark for correctly plotting the data, 1 mark for labelling the axes correctly, 1 mark for choosing a sensible scale, 1 mark for drawing a smooth curve of best fit. Allow plotting mark even if value calculated incorrectly in part a).]
d) Find the sucrose concentration where the curve of best fit crosses the x-axis / where there is no change in mass of the potato chip *[1 mark]*.

Topic 2 — Cells and Control

Page 16 — Mitosis

1 a) Prophase — the chromosomes condense *[1 mark]* and the membrane around the nucleus breaks down *[1 mark]*.
Telophase — membranes form around each new set of chromosomes *[1 mark]*, forming the nuclei of the two new cells *[1 mark]*.
b) A *[1 mark]*
The cells are diploid because they contain two copies of each chromosome (just like the original cell). They each contain exactly the same sets of chromosomes as each other, meaning they are genetically identical.
c) So the organism can grow. / So the organism can reproduce asexually. *[1 mark]*
2 a) A cell's DNA is duplicated *[1 mark]*, so that there will be one copy of the DNA for each new cell produced by mitosis *[1 mark]*.
b) i) anaphase *[1 mark]*
ii) Spindle fibres pull the chromosomes apart *[1 mark]* and then the chromatids are pulled to opposite ends of the cell *[1 mark]*.
c) The cytoplasm and cell membrane divide to form two separate cells *[1 mark]*.

Pages 17-18 — Cell Division and Growth

1 a) D *[1 mark]*
Cell division in a plant usually just happens in the meristems, which are found in the tips of roots and shoots.
b) cell elongation *[1 mark]*

2 a) To produce specialised cells *[1 mark]*.
Cell differentiation has the same purpose whatever the age of the animal — it has the same purpose in plants too.

b) Any two from: e.g. all growth in animals happens by cell division/animals don't grow by cell elongation, but growth in plants occurs by cell division and cell elongation. / Animals tend to grow while they're young, and then they reach full growth and stop growing, while plants often grow continuously. / In most animals, cell differentiation is lost at an early stage but plants continue to differentiate to develop new parts throughout their lives. *[2 marks — 1 mark for each correct answer.]*

3 a) A change in one of the genes that controls cell division *[1 mark]* causes cell to divide uncontrollably *[1 mark]*. This creates an abnormal mass of cells (a tumour) *[1 mark]*.

b) When the tumour invades and destroys surrounding tissue *[1 mark]*.

4 a) i) It's the 25th percentile *[1 mark]*. It shows the mass that 25% of children will have reached at a certain age *[1 mark]*.

ii) E.g. the child's weight was around the 50th percentile until it was 6 months of age *[1 mark]* but by 10 months it had increased to the 98th percentile *[1 mark]*. A doctor may be concerned because the child's weight has increased by more than two percentile lines in this time *[1 mark]*.

b) E.g. length/height *[1 mark]*, head circumference *[1 mark]*

5 a) Amount of growth between 0 and 60 weeks =
mass at 60 weeks − mass at birth = 120 − 20 = 100 kg
rate of growth = 100 kg ÷ 60 weeks = **1.7 kg week^{-1}**
[2 marks for correct final answer, otherwise 1 mark for 100 ÷ 60]

A rate is how much something changes over time. The animal's age in weeks is a measure of time in this question.

b) There would be no cell differentiation happening at the point marked X on the graph *[1 mark]*. This is because (for most animals) cell differentiation is lost at an early stage in life *[1 mark]*.

Remember, this is not true for plants — they continue to develop by cell differentiation throughout their life.

Page 19 — Stem Cells
Warm-Up
differentiate, specialised, early human embryos, growing, any cell type

1 a) C *[1 mark]*
Stem cells are cells which have not yet differentiated to become specialised cells. Gametes are cells needed for sexual reproduction (e.g. egg and sperm cells).

b) i) E.g. embryonic stem cells have the potential to produce any type of cell at all *[1 mark]*, whereas adult stem cells are less versatile *[1 mark]*.

ii) E.g. some people think it's wrong to destroy a potential human life *[1 mark]*.

c) meristem tissue *[1 mark]*
For this question it's no good writing 'the tips of roots' or 'the tips of shoots' — you've been asked to name the tissue that produces stem cells, not give its location within a plant.

2 Any two from: e.g. there may be a risk of tumour development *[1 mark]* if the rate at which the new insulin-secreting cells divide inside the patient can't be controlled *[1 mark]*. / There may be a risk of disease transmission from the donor to the recipient *[1 mark]* if viruses are present within the embryonic stem cells used to develop the new insulin-secreting cells *[1 mark]*. / There may be a risk of rejection/an immune response being triggered *[1 mark]* as the insulin-secreting cells have not been grown using the patient's own stem cells *[1 mark]*.

Page 20 — The Brain and Spinal Cord
1 a) D *[1 mark]*

b) The cerebrum is divided into the right and left cerebral hemispheres *[1 mark]*. It's responsible for, e.g. movement / intelligence / memory / language / vision *[1 mark for 2 correct functions]*.

c) The structure labelled X (the medulla oblongata) controls unconscious activities, such as heart rate/breathing *[1 mark]*. If drugs stop structure X/the medulla oblongata from functioning properly, heart rate/breathing could stop, which would be fatal *[1 mark]*.

2 a) i) The cerebellum *[1 mark]* because it is responsible for muscle coordination and balance *[1 mark]*.
Muscle coordination and balance are important to avoid being clumsy (e.g. to be able to carry things without dropping them or move around avoiding obstacles) and for walking normally.

ii) E.g. the tumour may be in a part of the brain which makes it difficult to access/surgically remove. / Treatments could lead to permanent brain damage. *[1 mark]*

b) Any two from: e.g. PET scans use radioactive chemicals to highlight parts of the brain, whereas CT scans don't *[1 mark]*. / PET scans can be used alone to investigate the structure and function of the brain whereas CT scans alone can only show structures *[1 mark]*. / PET scans can show brain structure and function in real time whereas CT scan can only take images of the brain *[1 mark]*.

Page 21 — The Nervous System
Warm-up
receptors, sensory, motor, effectors

1 a) i)

[1 mark]
Impulses travel along the axon, away from the cell body.

ii) Part X is the myelin sheath *[1 mark]*. It speeds up the electrical/nervous impulse along the neurone *[1 mark]*.

iii) Any two from: e.g. sensory neurones have one long dendron, whereas motor neurones have many short dendrites *[1 mark]*. / Sensory neurones have a cell body located in the middle of the neurone, whereas motor neurones have a cell body at one end *[1 mark]*. / Sensory neurones have a short axon, whereas motor neurones have a long axon *[1 mark]*.

b) The motor neurones don't work properly, so impulses don't get passed on from the CNS *[1 mark]* to the muscles involved in swallowing *[1 mark]*.

c) 58 cm = 0.58 m
0.58 ÷ 110 = 0.00527... s × 1000 = **5.27 ms**
[3 marks for the correct answer, otherwise 1 mark for 0.58 and 1 mark for 0.58 ÷ 110]

Page 22 — Synapses and Reflexes
1 a) C *[1 mark]*
Reflexes don't involve conscious parts of the brain — they're automatic and very fast (because you don't waste time thinking about the response).

b) i) relay neurone *[1 mark]*

ii) spinal cord *[1 mark]*, (an unconscious part of) the brain *[1 mark]*

iii) Sensory neurone *[1 mark]*. Its function is to carry nervous impulses from receptors to the central nervous system *[1 mark]*.

iv) To reduce the chance of the hand being injured by the flame. / To quickly move the hand away from the flame. *[1 mark]*

2 By preventing the release of neurotransmitters, opioids prevent information being transmitted across synapses *[1 mark]* between sensory neurones and (relay) neurones in the spinal cord *[1 mark]*. This means the information about the stimulus doesn't reach the brain, so no pain is felt *[1 mark]*.

Topic 3

Pages 23-24 — The Eye
Warm-Up

iris

cornea

lens

retina

optic nerve

1 a) i)   retina *[1 mark]*
       ii) Rods, which are sensitive in dim light *[1 mark]*. Cones, which
            are sensitive to different colours *[1 mark]*.
       iii) Red and green cones in the retina don't work properly *[1 mark]*.
    b)   The iris controls how much light enters the pupil *[1 mark]*.
2 a)   Cataracts are cloudy patches on the lens *[1 mark]*. The clouding
             of the lens stops light from being able to enter the eye normally
             [1 mark].
    b)   By replacing the faulty lens with an artificial one *[1 mark]*.
3 a)   It bends/refracts light into the eye *[1 mark]*.
    b)   It will change the amount by which the cornea bends/refracts
             light into the eye *[1 mark]*, which may mean that light is not
             focused onto the retina properly *[1 mark]*.
    c)   E.g. glasses / contact lenses / surgery to replace cornea *[1 mark]*.
4 a) i)   Behind the retina *[1 mark]*.
       ii)   Glasses with convex lenses *[1 mark]* can be used to make the
             light bend/refract so that it is brought into focus on the retina
             [1 mark].
    b)   The ciliary muscle contracts *[1 mark]*, which slackens the
             suspensory ligaments *[1 mark]*. This pulls the lens into a more
             rounded shape *[1 mark]* so light (from the nearby objects) is
             refracted more and is focused on the retina *[1 mark]*.

Topic 3 — Genetics

Page 25 — Sexual Reproduction and Meiosis
1 a)   D *[1 mark]*
    b)   D *[1 mark]*
    c)   zygote *[1 mark]*
2 a)

*[2 marks for the correct answer, otherwise 1 mark for two
X-shaped chromosomes]*
*A cell duplicates its DNA before meiosis, which is why the chromosomes are
X-shaped in Figure 1.*
    b)   Haploid gametes are needed so that when two gametes fuse at
         fertilisation *[1 mark]*, the resulting cell/zygote ends up with the
         full/diploid number of chromosomes *[1 mark]*.

Page 26 — Asexual and Sexual Reproduction
Warm-Up
Organisms reproduce in order to pass on their **genes**. Asexual reproduction
usually involves cell division by **mitosis**. It results in genetically **identical**
offspring. Sexual reproduction involves cell division by **meiosis**. It results
in genetically **different** offspring.
1 a)   Asexual reproduction because there is only one parent/no
         fertilisation *[1 mark]*.
    b)   Advantage: e.g. only one parent is needed, so the female can
         reproduce when conditions are favourable without having to wait
         for a mate *[1 mark]*.
         Disadvantage: e.g. it means there will be no genetic variation
         in the offspring, so the population may be more susceptible to
         disease/unfavourable changes in the environment *[1 mark]*.

2   Reproducing sexually creates genetic variation in the population
         of mint plants *[1 mark]*. This means that if there's an
         environmental change, it's more likely that some individuals will
         have the characteristics to survive the change *[1 mark]*. This
         would allow mint plants to evolve and become better adapted to
         their new environment *[1 mark]*.

Pages 27-28 — DNA
1 a)   A *[1 mark]*
    b)   A section of DNA that codes for a particular protein *[1 mark]*.
    c)   It is stored as chromosomes *[1 mark]*, which are long,
          coiled-up molecules of DNA *[1 mark]*.
2 a)   X = T/thymine *[1 mark]*, Y = G/guanine *[1 mark]*
    b) i) sugar *[1 mark]*, phosphate *[1 mark]*
       ii) sugar *[1 mark]*
    c)   It is made up of lots of repeating units (nucleotides) *[1 mark]*.
3 a)   salt *[1 mark]*, detergent *[1 mark]*
    b)   Add ice-cold alcohol to the boiling tube *[1 mark]*. This will
          make the DNA come out of solution (and form a precipitate) as
          DNA is not soluble in cold alcohol *[1 mark]*.
4 a)   hydrogen bonds *[1 mark]*
*You're told in the question that it's the bonds between bases on opposite DNA
strands that break and you should know that the pairs of bases on opposite
strands are held together by hydrogen bonds.*
    b)   Any two from: e.g. as the temperature increases, the percentage
          of denatured DNA in this sample increases. / The DNA in this
          sample only starts to denature above 62 °C. / All the DNA has
          denatured by 90 °C. / DNA denaturation in this sample is fastest
          between about 70 and 80 °C. *[1 mark for each correct answer,
          up to a maximum of 2 marks]*
    c)   % of DNA denatured at 70 °C = 25%
          25% of $8.14 \times 10^4 = (8.14 \times 10^4 \div 100) \times 25 = 20350$
          $= 2.04 \times 10^4$ base pairs *[2 marks for correct answer,
          or 1 mark for correctly calculating 25% of 8.14×10^4]*

Page 29 — Protein Synthesis
1 a)   C *[1 mark]*
*Each amino acid is coded for by a set of three bases. There are 14 bases in
total — that's four sets of three bases with two left over.*
    b) i) It will have a different sequence of bases *[1 mark]* due to a
          mutation *[1 mark]*.
       ii) The genetic variant may code for a different sequence of amino
           acids *[1 mark]*, which may change the shape of the protein
           being coded for *[1 mark]*. This could alter the protein's activity
           [1 mark], which could end up changing the flower colour of the
           plant *[1 mark]*.
2   Each of these proteins is coded for by a different gene *[1 mark]*.
         Each gene codes for a different sequence of amino acids
         [1 mark], which folds up to produce a different protein with
         a specific shape *[1 mark]*. Their different shapes allow the
         proteins to have different functions *[1 mark]*.

Pages 30-31 — More on Protein Synthesis
Warm-Up
In the first stage of protein synthesis, DNA is copied into mRNA.
This is called **transcription**. In the second stage of protein synthesis,
a protein is assembled according to the instructions in mRNA. This is
called **translation**. It takes place in the **cytoplasm** and is carried out by
ribosomes.
1 a)   C *[1 mark]*
*mRNA contains almost the same bases as DNA. The only difference is
T (thymine) is replaced by U (uracil).*
    b)   B *[1 mark]*
    c)   nucleus *[1 mark]*
    d)   (complementary) base pairing *[1 mark]*
    e)   It it joins together RNA nucleotides (to make mRNA) *[1 mark]*.
    f)   To carry the triplet code from DNA in the nucleus *[1 mark]*,
          to the ribosomes in the cytoplasm (where protein synthesis
          takes place) *[1 mark]*.

Answers

2 a) How to grade your answer:

Level 0: There is no relevant information. *[No marks]*

Level 1: There is some information about how a polypeptide is made from DNA. The points made are basic and not linked together. *[1 to 2 marks]*

Level 2: There is some explanation of how a polypeptide would be made from this section of DNA. Some of the points made are linked together. *[3 to 4 marks]*

Level 3: There is a clear and detailed explanation of how a polypeptide could be made from this section of DNA. The points made are well-linked and the answer has a clear and logical structure. *[5 to 6 marks]*

Here are some points your answer may include:
RNA polymerase binds to the region of non-coding DNA in front of the gene. The two DNA strands unzip and the RNA polymerase moves along one of the strands, using the coding DNA in the gene as a template to make mRNA. Base pairing ensures that the mRNA is complementary to the gene. Once made, the mRNA molecule moves out of the nucleus and joins to a ribosome in the cytoplasm. tRNA molecules bring amino acids to the ribosome — anticodons on the tRNA pair up with complementary codons in the mRNA to ensure that amino acids are brought to the ribosome in the correct order. The ribosome joins the amino acids together to make a polypeptide (protein).

b) The mutation may make it harder for RNA polymerase to bind to the non-coding region and begin transcription *[1 mark]*. This would mean that less mRNA is produced *[1 mark]* and so fewer polypeptides are translated overall *[1 mark]*.

Page 32 — The Work of Mendel

1 a) pea plants *[1 mark]*
   b) B *[1 mark]*
   c) Any two from: e.g. that hereditary units are passed on to offspring unchanged from the parents. / That an offspring inherits one hereditary unit for a characteristic from each parent. / That hereditary units can be dominant or recessive. *[2 marks — 1 mark for each correct answer]*

2 a) $382 \div 128 = 2.98$,
   so ratio of round seeds : wrinkly seeds = **3 : 1** *[1 mark]*
   b) E.g. that rounds seeds are dominant over wrinkly seeds. / That round seeds are dominant and wrinkly seeds are recessive. *[1 mark]*

Pages 33-34 — Genetic Diagrams

Warm-Up

genotype — The combination of alleles an organism has.
phenotype — The characteristics an organism has.
allele — A version of a gene.
heterozygous — Having two different alleles for a particular gene.
homozygous — Having two alleles the same for a particular gene.

1 No. The tall allele/T is dominant over the dwarf allele/t, so its presence will determine what characteristic is displayed in the phenotype *[1 mark]*. A tall plant could have the alleles TT or Tt *[1 mark]*.

2 a) E.g.

	N	N
n	Nn	Nn
n	Nn	Nn

[1 mark]

If you're given letters for the dominant and recessive alleles in the question, make sure you use them.

   b) E.g.

	N	n
N	NN	Nn
n	Nn	nn

[1 mark for a genetic diagram showing the correct genotypes of the parents and the offspring]
ratio of polled calves : horned calves = 3 : 1 *[1 mark]*

You could have drawn a different type of genetic diagram and still got the marks for Q2 b). Also, don't let the fact that there's one bull and multiple cows throw you — each separate cross between the bull and a cow produces a likely ratio of 3 : 1 polled calves : horned calves, so the overall ratio will still be 3 : 1.

3 a) BB *[1 mark]*, Bb *[1 mark]*
   b) i) E.g.

	B	b
b	Bb	bb
b	Bb	bb

[1 mark for a genetic diagram showing the correct genotypes of the parents and the offspring]
probability of offspring being a tabby: 50% / 0.5 / 1 in 2 *[1 mark]*

   ii) $6 \times 0.5 = 3$
   [1 mark for 3. Allow 1 mark if incorrect answer to part b) i) is used correctly here.]

4 Breed the short-haired hamster with a long-haired hamster *[1 mark]*. If any of the offspring have long hair, then the short-haired hamster must have the genotype Hh *[1 mark]*. If all the offspring have short hair, then the short-haired hamster could have the genotype HH or Hh *[1 mark]*. Further crosses would need to be done to confirm the genotype *[1 mark]*.

Page 35 — More Genetic Diagrams

1 a)

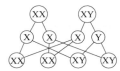

[1 mark]

   b) 50 : 50 *[1 mark]*

2 a) i) hh *[1 mark]*
      ii) hh *[1 mark]*, Hh *[1 mark]*

   b)

	H	h
H	HH	Hh
h	Hh	hh

[1 mark]
probability of having a child who does not have the disorder: 75% *[1 mark]*

Page 36 — Sex-Linked Genetic Disorders

1 a) A carrier is a person with only one copy of a recessive allele for a genetic disorder *[1 mark]*. They do not have disorder themselves, but they can pass the allele onto their offspring *[1 mark]*.

   b) i) 50% / 1 in 2 / 0.5 *[1 mark]*
      ii) 25% / 1 in 4 / 0.25 *[1 mark]*
   c) 50% / 1 in 2 / 0.5 *[1 mark]*

2 Females have two X chromosomes, so they need to inherit two recessive alleles in order to have the disorder *[1 mark]*. Males only need to inherit one recessive allele to develop the disorder, as they only have one X chromosome *[1 mark]*, so X-linked disorders are rarer in females than in males *[1 mark]*.

Page 37 — Inheritance of Blood Groups

Warm-Up
1) = true
2) = false
A person with blood group A can also have the genotype $I^A I^O$.
3) = false
There is only one gene for blood group in humans — but there are multiple alleles of that gene.
4) = false
A person with blood group O can have two parents with blood group A. Both of the parents would have to have one I^O allele, so they would each have the genotype $I^A I^O$.

Topic 4

1 a) They will have the blood group AB *[1 mark]* as neither allele is dominant over the other/both alleles determine the phenotype *[1 mark]*.
  b) The child could be blood group B if it inherits an I^B allele from one or both of its parents *[1 mark]*. The child could be blood group O if it inherits an I^O allele from both of its parents *[1 mark]*.
2 a) 3% *[1 mark]*
No one with the blood type AB can have an I^O allele. They must have the alleles I^A I^B. People with the blood type A or B could have an I^O allele though.
  b) 8 + 3 = **11%** OR 100 − 42 − 47 = **11%** *[2 marks for 11%, otherwise 1 mark for a correct working]*
Whichever method you used, you needed to realise that all the people with blood group AB and blood group B have the I^B allele.

Pages 38-39 — Variation
1 a) Phenotype is the characteristics an organism displays *[1 mark]*.
  b) C *[1 mark]*.
Mutations that have no effect on phenotype are most common, followed by mutations that only slightly affect the phenotype. It's very rare for a single mutation to have a large effect on an organism's phenotype, but it does happen.
2 a) sexual reproduction *[1 mark]*
  b) B *[1 mark]*
It's an acquired characteristic — a characteristic that an organism acquires (develops) during their lifetime.
  c) Figure 1 shows that this species of plant grows to different heights in different environments *[1 mark]*, which suggests that variation in height in this species is partly down to the environment *[1 mark]*. Figure 1 also shows that plants of this species grow to similar heights in the same environment *[1 mark]*, which suggests variation in height in this species is also partly genetic *[1 mark]*.
3 a) (0.42 + 0.41 + 0.48) ÷ 3 = 0.44
    (0.43 + 0.40 + 0.52) ÷ 3 = 0.45
    0.45 − 0.44 = **0.01** *[3 marks for the correct answer or 1 mark for 0.44 and 1 mark for 0.45]*
  b) Any three from: e.g. population 3 has the highest level of genetic variation in both years *[1 mark]*. / Genetic variation in populations changes over time *[1 mark]*. / Genetic variation in populations 1 and 3 increased over the ten-year period *[1 mark]*. / Genetic variation in population 2 decreased over the ten-year period *[1 mark]*.
  c) Lower because sexual reproduction increases genetic variation in a species *[1 mark]*. Without sexual reproduction, no new combinations of alleles would be produced in the offspring *[1 mark]*.

Page 40 — The Human Genome Project
1 a) To find every gene in the human genome *[1 mark]*.
  b) E.g. knowledge of genetic variations that affect how we respond to a disease/treatment could help scientists to develop drugs that are tailored to these variations *[1 mark]*. / Knowing how a disease affects us on a molecular level should make it possible to design more effective treatments with fewer side-effects *[1 mark]*.
  c) E.g. scientists are now able to identify the genes/alleles suspected of causing an inherited disorder much more quickly than they could do in the past *[1 mark]*. Once an allele that causes an inherited disorder has been identified, people can be tested for it. It may be possible to develop better treatments or even (eventually) a cure for the disease *[1 mark]*.
2 a) E.g. if testing identifies that a person has a genetic variant that increases their risk of developing late onset Alzheimer's *[1 mark]*, they may be able to make diet/lifestyle changes that could reduce their risk of developing the disease *[1 mark]*.
  b) E.g. it could cause increased stress for a person if they are identified as having a high risk genetic variant (and they may still never go on to develop Alzheimer's) *[1 mark]*. / A person with a high risk genetic variant may face discrimination from insurers *[1 mark]*.

Topic 4 — Natural Selection and Genetic Modification

Pages 41-42 — Natural Selection and Evidence for Evolution
Warm-up
beneficial, predation/competition, competition/predation, adapted to, offspring
1 a) B *[1 mark]*
  b) through mutation *[1 mark]*
2 a) They reproduce very rapidly *[1 mark]*.
  b) A mutation in the bacterium's DNA may give it resistance to the antibiotic *[1 mark]*.
  c) i) exposure to the antibiotic *[1 mark]*
    ii) Bacteria with the antibiotic resistance allele are more likely to survive than bacteria without the allele *[1 mark]* and so they reproduce many more times *[1 mark]*. This leads to the allele for antibiotic resistance being passed on to lots of offspring and so it becomes more common in the population *[1 mark]*.
3 a) They are more likely to survive if they are exposed to Warfarin™ *[1 mark]*. This means that they are more likely to pass their alleles on to the next generation *[1 mark]*.
  b) There was no Warfarin resistance in the population at the time the Warfarin was first introduced *[1 mark]*. After the introduction of Warfarin, the percentage of the rats with Warfarin resistance increased over time *[1 mark]*. This suggests that random mutations occurred that caused some rats to be resistant to Warfarin *[1 mark]*. After the introduction of Warfarin, the resistance allele then became more common in the population over time through natural selection *[1 mark]*.
4* How to grade your answer:
   Level 0: There is no relevant information. *[0 marks]*
   Level 1: There is some information about evolution by natural selection. The points made are basic and not linked together. *[1-2 marks]*
   Level 2: There is some explanation about how evolution by natural selection may lead to a change in the beak size of the finches. Some of the points made are linked together. *[3-4 marks]*
   Level 3: There is a clear and detailed explanation of how evolution by natural selection may lead to a change in the beak size of the finches. The points made are well-linked and the answer has a clear and logical structure. *[5-6 marks]*
Here are some points your answer may include:
After the storm, there will be fewer larger seeds available on the island. Birds with larger beaks will be less able to get food and seed size will become a selection pressure.
Small seeds will still be available, so birds with smaller beaks will be better adapted to their environment than the birds with larger beaks. This makes birds with smaller beaks more likely to survive and reproduce than birds with larger beaks.
In turn, this means that the alleles responsible for small beaks are more likely to be passed on to the next generation than the alleles for larger beaks. The alleles for smaller beaks will become more common in the population over time and eventually, all the finches in the population will have smaller beaks.

Page 43 — Darwin and Wallace
1 a) B *[1 mark]*
  b) Any two from: e.g. he noticed there was variation in members of the same species. / He noticed that those with characteristics most suited to their environment were more likely to survive. / He noticed that characteristics could be passed on to offspring. *[2 marks — 1 mark for each correct answer.]*
  c) E.g. he proposed that the bright colouration on many animals are warning signals to predators *[1 mark]*. This is an example of a beneficial characteristic that had evolved by natural selection *[1 mark]*.

Answers

2   Any two from: e.g. now that we understand evolutionary relationships, we can classify organisms based on their evolutionary ancestry. / Now that we understand how antibiotic-resistant bacteria evolve, we know that we have to keep developing new antibiotics. / Our understanding of the importance of genetic diversity and how it helps populations adapt to changing environments has influenced conservation projects to protect species.
[2 marks — 1 mark for each correct answer.]

Pages 44-45 — Fossil Evidence for Human Evolution
Warm-up
The timeline should have 'Ardi' at 4.4 million years ago, 'Lucy' at 3.2 million years ago and 'Turkana boy' at 1.6 million years ago.
1 a)   D *[1 mark]*
  b)   Any two from: e.g. Turkana Boy had longer legs than Ardi or Lucy. / Turkana Boy had shorter arms than Ardi and Lucy. / Turkana Boy had a larger brain size than Ardi and Lucy. / The structure of Turkana Boy's legs were more suitable to walking upright than those of Ardi or Lucy.
        [2 marks — 1 mark for each correct answer.]
2 a) i)   Specimen 1
   ii)   Specimen 3
   iii) Specimen 2
        [2 marks for all 3 answers to i)-iii) correct, or 1 mark for 1-2 answers correct.]
You should know the general trend in evolution of brain size in human ancestors — the more recent the species, the larger its brain is likely to be. So if you compare the brain sizes with the species on the timeline, you can see that Homo species have the largest, Australopithecus species are next on the scale and Ardipithecus species have the smallest brains.
  b)   E.g. they were shorter because they had shorter legs *[1 mark]*
3 a) i)   an opposable/ape-like big toe *[1 mark]*
   ii)   E.g. an ape-like big toe is needed for climbing trees/grasping branches *[1 mark]* and humans don't spend much time climbing trees/don't climb trees as much as chimpanzees *[1 mark]*
  b)   The two fossils show that human ancestors had a foot structure that was intermediate between that of a human and a chimpanzee *[1 mark]*
  c)   E.g. fossil B would have shorter arms/longer legs than a chimpanzee. / Fossil B would have a leg bone structure that allowed it to walk upright like a human, unlike a chimpanzee. *[1 mark]*

Page 46 — More Evidence for Evolution
1 a)   A pentadactyl limb is a limb with five digits *[1 mark]*
  b)   It suggests that they both evolved from the same common ancestor *[1 mark]*
2 a) i)   C, A, B *[1 mark]*
Remember that the oldest rock layers will be deeper, so any tools or fossils found in these layers will be older than ones found in the layers above.
   ii)   E.g. by studying the structural features of the tools *[1 mark]*. Using carbon-14 dating to date any carbon-containing material found with the tools *[1 mark]*.
  b)   Stone tools became more complex in shape over time *[1 mark]*, suggesting that the brain was getting larger and allowing human ancestors to create more complex tools *[1 mark]*.

Page 47 — Classification
1 a)   plants, animals, fungi, prokaryotes and protists *[1 mark]*
  b)   D *[1 mark]*
Remember, a species is the smallest group in the five kingdom classification system. Genus is the next smallest group.
2 a)   plants, animals and protists *[1 mark]*.
  b)   Archaea *[1 mark]*, Bacteria *[1 mark]*
3 a)   The DNA sequences for the same gene in different organisms can be compared *[1 mark]*. The more similar the DNA base sequences are to each other, the more closely related the organisms are *[1 mark]*.

  b)   Comparisons of RNA sequences led to the discovery that members of the prokaryote kingdom were not as closely related as previously thought *[1 mark]*, so it was suggested that the organisms in it were split into the two domains of Archaea and Bacteria *[1 mark]*.

Page 48 — Selective Breeding
1 a)   Any two from: e.g. to breed animals with higher meat/milk yields. / To breed crops with greater disease resistance. / To breed plants with bigger fruit.
        [2 marks — 1 mark for each correct answer.]
  b)   E.g. breeding animals to have a preference for alcohol *[1 mark]*.
2 a)   Select only those cows with a high milk yield for further breeding with males *[1 mark]*. Select the best offspring and breed them with each other *[1 mark]*. Continue to breed the most desirable offspring over several generations, so that the milk yield gets bigger and bigger *[1 mark]*.
  b)   The selective breeding of the cows has reduced the gene pool for his herd *[1 mark]*. A smaller gene pool means that it's more likely that individuals will inherit harmful genetic defects, such as Weaver Syndrome *[1 mark]*.
  c)   There's less genetic variation in the new herd, because they have been selectively bred *[1 mark]*. This means that there's less chance of there being any alleles in the herd that would give the cows resistance to bovine tuberculosis *[1 mark]*. The cattle are closely related, so if one individual gets the disease, the others are also likely to succumb to it *[1 mark]*.

Page 49 — Tissue Culture
1 a)   They are genetically identical *[1 mark]*.
  b)   Any two from: e.g. many plants can be grown very quickly. / Plants can be grown in little space. / Plants can be grown all year round. / You can create lines of plants with the same beneficial/desirable features. *[2 marks — 1 mark for each correct answer.]*
  c)   C *[1 mark]*
Shoot tips are best for plant tissue culture because they're fast-growing.
2 a)   Using animal tissue cultures allows scientists to investigate the effects of a drug on a single animal tissue, without the complications of a whole organism *[1 mark]*.
  b)   Extract a sample of liver cells from a rat *[1 mark]*. Add enzymes to the sample of tissue to separate the cells from each other *[1 mark]*. Place the separated cells in a culture vessel containing a growth medium with all of the nutrients that they need to grow and divide *[1 mark]*. After several rounds of cell division, split cells into separate vessels to encourage further growth *[1 mark]*.

Pages 50-51 — Genetic Engineering
Warm-up
restriction enzyme — cuts DNA open
plasmid — a type of vector
ligase — sticks DNA ends together
GM organism — an organism with DNA from a different species
vector — transfers DNA into a cell
1 a) i)   A restriction enzyme would be used to cut the gene out of the organism's genome *[1 mark]*.
   ii)   The vector is cut using the same restriction enzyme that was used to isolate the desired gene *[1 mark]*. The ligase enzyme is used to join the vector DNA and the desired gene together (at their sticky ends) *[1 mark]*. The resulting recombinant DNA/vector containing the desired gene can then be inserted into a bacterial cell *[1 mark]*.
  b)   B *[1 mark]*
  c)   E.g. bacteria can be grown in large numbers *[1 mark]* so the desired protein can be produced in large quantities *[1 mark]*.
2 a)   E.g. herbicide resistance / additional nutrients / improved drought resistance *[1 mark]*.

Topic 5

b) Any two from: e.g. some people worry that if transplanted genes escape into the environment, they may be picked up by other plants, resulting in superweeds. / Some people worry that GM crops could have a negative impact on food chains/human health. *[1 mark for each correct answer. Maximum of 2 marks.]*

3 How to grade your answer:
Level 0: There is no relevant information. *[0 marks]*
Level 1: There is some information about the advantages of the scientist's findings or concerns about genetic engineering. The points made are basic and not linked together. *[1-2 marks]*
Level 2: There is some discussion about the potential advantages of the scientist's findings, as well as concerns about genetic engineering. Some of the points made are linked together. *[3-4 marks]*
Level 3: There is a clear and detailed discussion about the potential advantages of the scientist's findings, as well as concerns about genetic engineering. The points made are well-linked and the answer has a clear and logical structure. *[5-6 marks]*

Here are some points your answer may include:
Advantages:
The hens may be genetically engineered to produce proteins used in drugs/to treat human diseases in their eggs. These proteins might include insulin for diabetes or antibodies used in therapy for arthritis/cancer/MS.
The hens may be genetically engineered to produce proteins for medical research in their eggs.
They may be genetically engineered to produce eggs with extra nutrients for human consumption.
Concerns:
There may be unforeseen consequences of inserting human DNA into the hens' DNA. For example, some hens may suffer from health problems later in life as a result of being genetically engineered. Many embryos may not survive the genetic engineering process.
There may be an impact on food chains as a result of genetically engineering the hens.
There may be adverse consequences for human health if the eggs are used for human consumption.

Page 52 — GMOs and Human Population Growth

1 a) *Bacillus thuringiensis* produces a toxin which kills many insect larvae *[1 mark]*. The gene for the toxin can be cut out of the bacterial DNA and inserted into the DNA of the crop plant *[1 mark]*. The crop plant will then produce the toxin in its stems and leaves and the crop will be resistant to the insect pests *[1 mark]*.
b) E.g. the long term effects of exposure to the *Bacillus thuringiensis* toxin are unknown *[1 mark]*. There's a danger that the insects will develop resistance to the toxin *[1 mark]*.
2 a) Crops may be genetically modified to survive/grow better in drought conditions *[1 mark]*, leading to higher yields *[1 mark]* and therefore more food for the population *[1 mark]*.
b) Advantage: biological control methods can have longer lasting effects than chemical pesticides. / They can be less harmful to wildlife than chemical pesticides. *[1 mark]*
Disadvantage: introducing new organisms can cause problems, e.g. a new organism may become a pest itself *[1 mark]*.

Topic 5 — Health, Disease and the Development of Medicines

Pages 53-54 — Health and Disease

Warm-up
Chalara ash dieback — fungus, Ebola — virus, Tuberculosis — bacterium, Malaria — protist, Cholera — bacterium
1 a) Health is a state of complete physical, mental and social well-being *[1 mark]*, and not merely the absence of disease or infirmity *[1 mark]*.

b) A communicable disease can be transmitted between individuals (by a pathogen), whereas a non-communicable disease can not *[1 mark]*.
2 a) C *[1 mark]*
b) i) The pathogen is spread orally so could be transmitted by drinking contaminated water *[1 mark]*. Proper drainage systems should mean water sources are less likely to be contaminated *[1 mark]*.
ii) E.g. cholera *[1 mark]*
3 a) E.g. leaf loss *[1 mark]* and bark lesions *[1 mark]*.
b) E.g. carried by the wind / by import of diseased trees from affected areas in Europe *[1 mark]*.
c) E.g. young, infected trees could be removed and new species replanted in their place *[1 mark]*. / The import of ash trees could be restricted to prevent any further infected trees entering the country *[1 mark]*.
4 How to grade your answer:
Level 0: There is no relevant information. *[0 marks]*
Level 1: There is some explanation about how mosquito nets could help to protect people against malaria. The points made are basic and not linked together. *[1 to 2 marks]*
Level 2: There is some explanation about why people in high altitude areas should learn how to use mosquito nets. Some of the points made are linked together. *[3 to 4 marks]*
Level 3: There is a clear and detailed explanation about why people in high altitude areas should learn how to use mosquito nets. The points made are well-linked and the answer has a clear and logical structure. *[5 to 6 marks]*

Here are some points your answer may include:
Mosquitoes are animal vectors for *Plasmodium*. / Mosquitoes transmit *Plasmodium* between people when they bite them. Mosquito nets prevent mosquitoes from biting humans at night. Climate change may mean that *Plasmodium* is able to mature at higher altitudes than was previously possible. This means that *Plasmodium* may become more common at higher altitudes. Therefore people at higher altitudes will be more at risk of developing malaria in the future. By learning how to use mosquito nets, people living at higher altitudes will be able to reduce this risk of developing malaria in the future.

Pages 55-56 — Viruses and STIs

1 a) a bacterium *[1 mark]*
b) By sexual contact *[1 mark]*.
c) E.g. using a condom during sex *[1 mark]*.
2 a) During the lysogenic stage of its life cycle the virus is dormant *[1 mark]*, which means that the virus is not active and so will not be causing any symptoms in the infected person *[1 mark]*.
b) HIV kills white blood cells, which are an important part of the immune response *[1 mark]*. This means that the person is more vulnerable to infection by other pathogens *[1 mark]*.
c) HIV is spread via bodily fluids *[1 mark]*. By sharing needles there's a risk of injecting infected bodily fluids/blood from the previous user of the needle *[1 mark]*.
HIV isn't just spread through sexual contact, although that's a common means of transmission.
3 a) The virus injects its genetic material into the host cell *[1 mark]*. It then uses proteins and enzymes in the host cell to replicate its genetic material and produce the components of new viruses *[1 mark]*. The viral components assemble into new viruses *[1 mark]*, then the host cell splits open releasing the new viruses *[1 mark]*.
b) Viruses do not have the components/proteins and enzymes necessary to reproduce by themselves *[1 mark]*.
4 a) The virus has a lysogenic pathway in its life cycle *[1 mark]*.
In a lysogenic pathway the genetic material of a virus becomes incorporated into the DNA of the host cell.

Answers

b) The UV radiation acted as a trigger for the viral DNA to exit the genome of the host *[1 mark]*. Then the viral DNA entered the lytic cycle *[1 mark]*, so the proteins and enzymes of the host cell were used to make new components of the virus *[1 mark]*. The viral components assembled into new viruses and the cells burst *[1 mark]*.

Don't forget that some kind of trigger can eventually lead to viral genetic material leaving the lysogenic cycle and entering into the lytic cycle — in this case it's UV radiation.

Page 57 — Plant Diseases

1 a) E.g. it provides a barrier to stop pathogens entering a leaf / it provides a barrier to stop pests damaging a leaf / it prevents water from collecting on the leaf and so reduces the risk of infection by pathogens transmitted via water *[1 mark]*.

b) E.g. plants produce antiseptics which kill some (fungal/bacterial) pathogens / plants produce chemicals that deter pests from feeding on their leaves *[1 mark]*.

2 a) He could add nutrients to the soils of the affected plants *[1 mark]* and observe whether or not the symptoms disappear *[1 mark]*.

b) Different pathogens disperse in different ways, so the distribution of the infected plants may indicate what method of dispersal is used by the pathogen *[1 mark]*.

c) E.g. monoclonal antibodies that are complementary to antigens on the bacteria *[1 mark]*.

Page 58 — Fighting Disease

1 a) E.g. skin / mucus / cilia *[1 mark]*.

b) D *[1 mark]*

c) Hydrochloric acid *[1 mark]*

2 a) The immune response to a specific pathogen *[1 mark]*.

b) B-lymphocytes detect antigens on a pathogen in the blood *[1 mark]*. The B-lymphocytes produce specific antibodies *[1 mark]*, which lock on to the pathogen and destroy it *[1 mark]*. The antibodies are then produced rapidly and flow throughout the body to find all similar pathogens *[1 mark]*.

3 Cells that line the airways in the lungs have cilia *[1 mark]*, which sweep mucus containing any trapped pathogens out of the lungs *[1 mark]*. If the cilia don't work properly then pathogens will remain in the lungs and will be more likely to cause infections *[1 mark]*.

Pages 59-60 — Memory Lymphocytes and Immunisation

1 a) D *[1 mark]*

b) E.g. sometimes people may have a bad reaction to a vaccine *[1 mark]*.

c) Their immune system can respond quickly if the pathogen which causes the disease enters their body again *[1 mark]*.

2 a) A *[1 mark]*

b) At the time of the second exposure the body has some memory lymphocytes that will recognise the pathogen's antigens *[1 mark]* and trigger more antibodies to be made *[1 mark]*. This means antibodies are produced much more quickly following the second exposure (so the curve is steeper) *[1 mark]*.

3 a) It would prevent the traveller from catching cholera whilst they are visiting the country *[1 mark]* and then bringing it back to their own country *[1 mark]*.

b) It prevents anyone from bringing certain diseases into the country *[1 mark]*.

4 a) To kill/inactivate the virus *[1 mark]*.

b) Their body would respond to the vaccine by producing antibodies and memory lymphocytes *[1 mark]*. Because of this, if the virus enters their body again, their immune system will recognise the foreign antigens and respond more quickly *[1 mark]*, meaning they will be more likely to eradicate the virus before it causes polio *[1 mark]*.

c) If many people in a population are immunised, then there will be fewer people who are likely to catch the disease and pass it on to others *[1 mark]*. This means that even if some individuals cannot be immunised, they are less likely to come into contact with someone with the disease and so are less likely to catch it *[1 mark]*.

Pages 61-62 — Monoclonal Antibodies

Warm-up

lymphocytes, dye, attach to

1 a) A *[1 mark]*

b) So that the animal makes B-lymphocytes/antigen-producing cells which produce antibodies *[1 mark]* that are complementary to the antigen that's injected *[1 mark]*.

c) i) C *[1 mark]*

ii) Tumour cells divide rapidly *[1 mark]* so using them means the hybridoma cell will divide rapidly to produce many clones *[1 mark]*, which can produce more of the monoclonal antibodies *[1 mark]*.

2 To use the test, the woman should urinate on the patch containing the blue beads *[1 mark]*. If hCG is present in her urine, then the monoclonal antibodies on the blue beads will attach to the hormone *[1 mark]*. The urine carries the beads and the hormone to the test strip, where they bind to the antibodies secured on the strip *[1 mark]*. The test strip will then turn blue, showing a positive result *[1 mark]*.

3 a) Monoclonal antibodies allow the specific targeting of drugs to cancer cells *[1 mark]*. This means that fewer body cells are affected compared with normal drug and radiotherapy treatments *[1 mark]*, so there are fewer side effects *[1 mark]*.

b) Monoclonal antibodies have been developed that bind to the proteins which form blood clots *[1 mark]*. These antibodies can be labelled with a radioactive element and injected into the bloodstream *[1 mark]*. A camera which detects radiation can then be used to visualise where the antibodies have accumulated, and so the position of any blood clots *[1 mark]*.

Page 63 — Antibiotics and Other Medicines

1 a) i) D *[1 mark]*

In preclinical trials, animals are used to test the drug on a whole body or multiple body systems, so the animal needs to be alive. You wouldn't want to test on humans at this stage, just in case the drug proves to be dangerous.

ii) E.g. toxicity / efficacy / dosage *[1 mark]*

b) In case the drug has any harmful effects *[1 mark]*.

c) i) To ensure that any effect of the drug is due to the drug itself and not because the patient is expecting to feel better *[1 mark]*.

A placebo is a substance that's like the drug being tested but doesn't do anything.

ii) So that neither the patients nor the doctors are able to subconsciously influence the results of the trials *[1 mark]*.

In a double-blind trial neither the patient nor the doctor knows whether the patient is receiving the drug or a placebo.

2 a) Antibiotics kill/prevent the growth of bacterial cells *[1 mark]*, but they do not harm human cells *[1 mark]*.

b) Viruses can only reproduce inside their host's cells *[1 mark]*. This means that it is very hard to develop drugs which target the virus but not the cells of the host *[1 mark]*.

Pages 64-65 — Investigating Antibiotics and Antiseptics

1 a) A *[1 mark]*

b) radius = 7.5 mm ($\pm$ 1 mm)
area = πr^2 = 3.14 × 7.5^2 = **177 mm^2** *[3 marks for correct answer using a radius of 7.5 $\pm$ 1 mm, otherwise 1 mark for a radius of 7.5 $\pm$ 1 mm and 1 mark for area = πr^2]*

Make sure you either measure the radius from exactly in the middle of the circle, or that you measure the diameter of the circle and divide it by 2.

c) The bacteria in culture 2 are resistant to antibiotic B *[1 mark]*, so the antibiotic doesn't kill the bacteria to create a clear zone/an inhibition zone *[1 mark]*.

Topic 6

d) i) mean = $(85 + 76 + 12 + 80) \div 4$
= $253 \div 4 =$ **63 mm²** *[2 marks for correct answer, otherwise 1 mark for 85 + 76 + 12 + 80 = 253]*

ii) E.g. the result is an anomaly / not enough antibiotic used / a lower concentration of antibiotic used. *[1 mark]*

2 a) radius = 4.0 mm ($\pm$ 0.5 mm)
area = $\pi r^2 = 3.14 \times 4.0^2 =$ **50.2 mm²** *[3 marks for correct answer using radius of 4.0 mm $\pm$ 0.5 mm, otherwise 1 mark for radius = 4.0 mm $\pm$ 0.5 mm and 1 mark for area = πr^2]*

b) E.g. use an autoclave to sterilise the Petri dish and the agar before using them *[1 mark]*. Keep the Petri dish covered while it is drying *[1 mark]*.

c) E.g. pass the inoculating loop through a hot flame before using it *[1 mark]*. Only remove the lid of the culture vial very briefly when transferring the bacteria *[1 mark]*.

d) The bacteria has not been evenly spread across the agar *[1 mark]*, so it would be very difficult to calculate the size of inhibition zones around different antiseptics on the plate *[1 mark]*.

Page 66 — Non-Communicable Diseases

1 a) It is a factor associated with an increased likelihood of getting a disease *[1 mark]*.

b) When alcohol is broken down in the liver, toxic products are released *[1 mark]*. Too many of these toxic products can cause permanent liver damage/liver disease *[1 mark]*.

c) E.g. cardiovascular disease *[1 mark]*

2 How to grade your answer:
Level 0: There is no relevant information. *[No marks]*
Level 1: There is a brief explanation of the lifestyle factors likely to be tackled and the economical reasons behind the campaign. The points made are basic and not linked together. *[1 to 2 marks]*
Level 2: There is some explanation of the lifestyle factors likely to be tackled and the economical reasons behind the campaign. Some of the points made are linked together. *[3 to 4 marks]*
Level 3: There is a clear and detailed explanation of the lifestyle factors likely to be tackled and the economical reasons behind the campaign. The points made are well-linked and the answer has a clear and logical structure. *[5 to 6 marks]*
Here are some points your answer may include:
The campaign is likely to encourage children to eat healthily and exercise. If children eat more healthily and exercise then they are less likely to become overweight or obese. Healthy children are then less likely to grow up to become overweight or obese. Obesity is a risk factor for many other non-communicable diseases, so healthy children are also less likely to suffer from other non-communicable diseases, such as type 2 diabetes, later in life. This means that there will be less pressure on the resources of local hospitals and the National Health Service as a whole to treat people with obesity and related health issues. This also means that more people in society will be able to work and contribute to the UK's economy. Since fewer resources are being spent on helping people with obesity and obesity-related health issues and there are more people contributing to the economy, this means that the scheme should be beneficial for society as a whole.

Page 67 — Measures of Obesity

1 a) waist-to-hip ratio = waist circumference ÷ hips circumference
= $91 \div 84 =$ **1.1** *[1 mark]*

b) i) 170 cm = 1.70 m
BMI = mass(kg) ÷ height (m)² = $73.5 \div 1.70^2$
25.4 kg m⁻² *[3 marks for correct answer, otherwise 1 mark for 1.70 m and 1 mark for BMI = mass (kg) ÷ height (m)²]*

ii) E.g. she has dropped a lot of weight in a short amount of time / if she loses much more weight she may become underweight *[1 mark]*.

2 a) Patient C because she has a high BMI and her waist-to-hip ratio indicates she is obese *[1 mark]*. Being obese is a risk factor for cardiovascular disease *[1 mark]*.

b) Her body mass may be high in relation to her height because she has a lot of muscle (rather than fat) *[1 mark]*. This would mean she has a high BMI but is not likely to be at risk of developing obesity-related disorders *[1 mark]*.

Page 68 — Treatments for Cardiovascular Disease

Warm-up
heart, blood pressure, arteries, strokes

1 a) Any two from: e.g. cut down on foods high in saturated fat / eat a healthy, balanced diet *[1 mark]* / quit smoking *[1 mark]* / exercise regularly *[1 mark]* / lose weight if necessary *[1 mark]*.

b) i) A stent could be inserted into the artery *[1 mark]* to keep the artery open and maintain blood flow to the heart *[1 mark]*.

ii) Any two from: e.g. there is a risk of infection *[1 mark]*, there is a risk of bleeding *[1 mark]* / there is a risk of developing blood clots *[1 mark]* / there is a risk that the artery might narrow again *[1 mark]*.

c) Any two from: e.g. statins *[1 mark]*, these reduce his blood cholesterol levels *[1 mark]*. / Anticoagulants *[1 mark]*, these make blood clots less likely *[1 mark]*. / Antihypertensives *[1 mark]*, these reduce blood pressure *[1 mark]*.

Topic 6 — Plant Structures and Their Functions

Pages 69-70 — Photosynthesis

Warm-up
algae, light, glucose, chloroplasts

1 a) carbon dioxide + water $\longrightarrow$ glucose + oxygen *[1 mark]*

b) A *[1 mark]*

2 a) E.g. building the plant's biomass *[1 mark]*.

b) Energy stored in the biomass of photosynthetic organisms is transferred along food chains *[1 mark]* as animals eat these organisms and each other *[1 mark]*. That means that many organisms rely on photosynthesis as a source of energy/biomass *[1 mark]*.

3 a) oxygen *[1 mark]*

b) $1.2 \div 2 =$ **0.6 cm³ h⁻¹** *[1 mark]*

c) i) As the distance from the lamp increases, the rate of gas production decreases *[1 mark]*. This is because the intensity of the light reaching the plant decreases as the test tube is placed further away *[1 mark]*, and light intensity is a limiting factor for photosynthesis *[1 mark]*.

ii) E.g. by repeating the experiment with more distances from the light source / at greater distances from the light source *[1 mark]*.

d) E.g. different lamps may produce different intensities of light *[1 mark]*, so using the same lamp helps to ensure that the distance between the lamp and the test tube is the only thing affecting the light intensity *[1 mark]*.

Page 71 — Limiting Factors in Photosynthesis

1 a) the inverse square law *[1 mark]*

b) The light intensity reaching the plant would be four times greater *[1 mark]*.

The inverse square law is light intensity $\propto 1/d^2$. This means that as the square of the distance decreases, light intensity increases proportionally — in other words, if you halve the distance, the light intensity will be four times greater.

c) As carbon dioxide concentration increases, the rate of photosynthesis also increases *[1 mark]*, until carbon dioxide is no longer the limiting factor and the rate stays the same *[1 mark]*.

2 a) The rate of photosynthesis increases between points A and B *[1 mark]*. This is because increasing the temperature (up to the optimum) increases the rate at which the enzymes involved in photosynthesis work *[1 mark]*.

Answers

b)   Increasing the temperature after point B causes the rate of photosynthesis to fall *[1 mark]*. This is because the temperatures are too high for the enzymes involved in photosynthesis to work *[1 mark]*. At point C, no photosynthesis is occurring because all the enzymes are denatured *[1 mark]*.

Page 72 — Transport in Plants
Warm-up
A. living cells, B. dead cells, C. end wall with pores,
D. lignin, E. phloem tube, F. xylem tube
1 a) i)   E.g. sucrose *[1 mark]*
     ii) E.g. water *[1 mark]*, mineral ions *[1 mark]*
  b)   A *[1 mark]*
Transport via the phloem is called translocation (not transpiration) and it requires energy to happen. It transports substances all over the plant, from the roots to the leaves and in the opposite direction.
2 a) *Pythium* destroys root hair cells and therefore decreases the surface area available for the absorption of water from the soil *[1 mark]*. This will mean that less water will be available to be drawn up from the roots by the transpiration stream *[1 mark]*.
  b)   If the root hair cells are destroyed, a plant will have difficulty absorbing mineral ions from the soil *[1 mark]*. The disruption to the transpiration stream will also reduce the plant's ability to transport mineral ions from the roots to where they're needed in the plant *[1 mark]*.

Pages 73-74 — Stomata and Transpiration
1 a) To allow gas exchange/the movement of carbon dioxide and oxygen into and out of a plant *[1 mark]*.
  b)   guard cells *[1 mark]*
  c)   Water vapour diffuses out of leaves through the stomata *[1 mark]*. When the stomata are open, water is able to diffuse out of the leaves and more water is pulled up the plant by transpiration *[1 mark]*. When the stomata are closed, less water is able to diffuse out of the leaves and so less water is pulled up the plant by transpiration *[1 mark]*.
2 a) To stop the loss of water by evaporation *[1 mark]*.
  b)

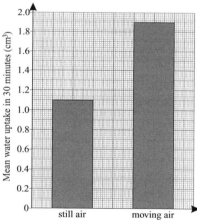

[1 mark for correctly drawn bars, 1 mark for correctly labelled axes / drawn to a sensible scale.]
  c)   The greater the air flow around the plant, the greater the transpiration rate *[1 mark]*.
  d)   E.g. increasing air flow carries more water vapour away from the plant/reduces the concentration of water vapour outside the leaves *[1 mark]*. This increases the rate of diffusion of water from the leaf cells to the air *[1 mark]*.
  e)   rate of transpiration = mean volume of water uptake ÷ time
        30 minutes ÷ 60 = 0.5 hours
        1.9 ÷ 0.5 = **3.8 cm³ hour⁻¹** *[2 marks for the correct answer, otherwise 1 mark for 1.9 ÷ 0.5]*

Page 75 — Adaptations of Leaves and Plants
1 a) Plant C *[1 mark]*. Plant C has a low number of stomata and plants in very dry environments are likely to have fewer stomata *[1 mark]* to limit the amount of water lost through the stomata by transpiration/evaporation *[1 mark]*.
  b)   E.g. small/curled leaves / small leaves/spines instead of leaves / thick waxy cuticles / a thick fleshy stem to store water / stomata that only open at night / stomata sunken in pits *[1 mark]*
2   How to grade your answer:
      Level 0: There is no relevant information. *[0 marks]*
      Level 1: There is some explanation about how leaves are adapted for photosynthesis. The points made are basic and not linked together. *[1-2 marks]*
      Level 2: There is some explanation about how leaves are adapted for photosynthesis. Some of the points made are linked together. *[3-4 marks]*
      Level 3: There is a clear and detailed explanation about how leaves are adapted for photosynthesis. The points made are well-linked and the answer has a clear and logical structure. *[5-6 marks]*
      Here are some points your answer may include:
      Leaves are broad to catch lots of light, which is needed for photosynthesis. The upper epidermis of the leaves is transparent to allow light to pass through to the palisade layer underneath. The palisade layer contains lots of chloroplasts to capture the light. Water is also needed for photosynthesis and is supplied to the leaves by the xylem tissue. A waxy cuticle on the top layer of the leaf allows light to pass through, but helps to reduce water loss by evaporation. Stomata allow carbon dioxide to enter the leaf for photosynthesis, but they can close to limit water loss when water availability is low. The spongy mesophyll tissue contains air spaces, to increase the rate of diffusion of carbon dioxide into and out of the leaf's cells.

Page 76 — Plant Hormones
Warm-up
false, true, false, true
1 a) The seedlings in Set A have grown straight up but the seedlings in Set B have grown sideways (towards the light) *[1 mark]*.
  b)   It allows the plant to receive maximum light for photosynthesis *[1 mark]*.
  c)   Auxin accumulated on the shaded side of the shoots / the side of the shoots away from the light *[1 mark]*. The auxin made the cells elongate/grow faster on the shaded side, so the shoots bent/grew towards the light *[1 mark]*.
  d)   In the roots of a plant, auxin inhibits cell elongation *[1 mark]*, whereas in the shoots of a plant, auxin promotes cell elongation *[1 mark]*.

Pages 77-78 — Commercial Uses of Plant Hormones
1 a) A *[1 mark]*
  b)   Transporting them will take time *[1 mark]*. By picking them before they are ripe, they will still be fresh when they reach the supermarket / they will be firm and not as easily damaged while being transported *[1 mark]*.
2 a) i)   germination *[1 mark]*
     ii) gibberellin *[1 mark]*
  b) i)   E.g. auxin *[1 mark]*, because the root is growing down/towards gravity and the shoot is growing up/towards the light / because auxins promote root and shoot growth *[1 mark]*.
     ii) E.g. in rooting powders / in weedkillers *[1 mark]*
3 a) auxin *[1 mark]*
  b)   The weeds have broad leaves and the crops have narrow leaves *[1 mark]*. The auxin/weedkiller only affects broad-leaved plants *[1 mark]*.

4   How to grade your answer:
     Level 0:   There is no relevant information. *[0 marks]*
     Level 1:   There is some explanation about how gibberellins
                might be used to grow seedless grapes or improve
                grape quality, or about how grapes could be grown all
                year round. The points made are basic and not linked
                together. *[1-2 marks]*
     Level 2:   There is some explanation about how gibberellins
                might be used to grow large, high quality seedless
                grapes, which can be grown all year round. Some of
                the points made are linked together. *[3-4 marks]*
     Level 3:   There is a clear and detailed explanation about how
                gibberellins might be used to grow large, high quality
                seedless grapes, which can be grown all year round.
                The points made are well-linked and the answer has a
                clear and logical structure. *[5-6 marks]*
     Here are some points your answer may include:
     Gibberellins might be used to promote seed germination at times
     of the year when it wouldn't normally happen. This would allow
     grapes to be grown all year round. Gibberellins might be used
     to promote stem growth in the grape vines, so that more grapes
     can be grown/a greater yield can be produced in a shorter period
     of time/the crop grows at a time of year when it normally would
     not. Gibberellins might also be used to reduce flower formation
     so that grape quality is improved and grape size increases.
     By applying gibberellins to unpollinated flowers, grapes will
     grow but the seeds will not.

*The way that seedless grapes are produced is a little different to the method
used to produce other seedless fruits, but you wouldn't be expected to know this
in an exam. Just use your knowledge of the kinds of things that gibberellins can
be used for and apply it to the context given in the question.*

Topic 7 — Animal Coordination, Control and Homeostasis

Page 79 — Hormones

1 a)   C *[1 mark]*
  b)   C *[1 mark]*
  c)   A — pituitary *[1 mark]*, B — thyroid *[1 mark]*, C — adrenal
       [1 mark], D — pancreas *[1 mark]*, E — ovary *[1 mark]*
  d)   Any two from: e.g. the endocrine system uses hormones rather
       than electrical/nervous impulses *[1 mark]*. / In the endocrine
       system messages travel via the blood rather than via neurones
       [1 mark]. / The effects of the endocrine system are slower
       [1 mark]. / The effects of the endocrine system are longer lasting
       [1 mark].
2 a)   bones *[1 mark]*
  b)   Testes produce testosterone *[1 mark]* so having the testes
       removed will mean there's less testosterone acting on the bones,
       therefore increasing the risk of bones becoming brittle *[1 mark]*.

Page 80 — Adrenaline and Thyroxine

Warm-up
Clockwise from top left: **increase in** level of hormone detected, release
of hormone **inhibited**, **normal** level of hormone, release of hormone
stimulated, **decrease in** level of hormone detected.
1 a)   adrenal glands *[1 mark]*
  b)   E.g. it increases heart rate / blood pressure / blood flow to the
       muscles / the blood glucose level *[1 mark]*.
  c)   fight or flight *[1 mark]*
2 a)   E.g. it regulates metabolic rate *[1 mark]*.
  b)   When the blood thyroxine level becomes higher than normal,
       release of TRH/thyrotropin releasing hormone is inhibited
       [1 mark]. This reduces the production of TSH/thyroid
       stimulating hormone *[1 mark]*, meaning the thyroid gland is not
       stimulated to produce thyroxine, so the blood thyroxine level
       falls *[1 mark]*.

Page 81 — The Menstrual Cycle

1 a)   ovary *[1 mark]*
  b)   FSH/follicle-stimulating hormone *[1 mark]*
  c)   It causes it to thicken and grow *[1 mark]*.
2 a)   A *[1 mark]*
*Oestrogen and progesterone are involved in the growth and maintenance of the
uterus lining, so menstruation (the breakdown of the uterus lining) occurs during
time period A when the levels of these two hormones are low.*
  b)   E.g.

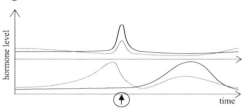

*[1 mark for arrow drawn in line with the LH peak or its
rapid descent]*
Remember, the rapid increase in LH is what stimulates ovulation.
  c)   FSH/follicle-stimulating hormone *[1 mark]*
  d)   After ovulation, the remains of the follicle develop into a
       corpus luteum *[1 mark]*, which secretes progesterone *[1 mark]*.
       Progesterone maintains the uterus lining *[1 mark]*.

Pages 82-83 — Controlling Fertility

1 a)   E.g. (male/female) condom / diaphragm *[1 mark]*.
  b)   They prevent sperm from meeting an egg *[1 mark]*.
  c)   E.g. some barrier methods (condoms) can protect against
       sexually transmitted infections/STIs, unlike hormonal methods
       [1 mark]. Barrier methods don't have unpleasant side-effects,
       such as headaches/mood changes/acne, like hormonal methods
       can *[1 mark]*.
2 a)   If the woman doesn't ovulate regularly, then there is less chance
       that an egg will be present to be fertilised by a sperm after sexual
       intercourse *[1 mark]*.
  b)   Clomifene therapy causes more FSH and LH *[1 mark]* to be
       produced by the body, which stimulate egg maturation and
       ovulation *[1 mark]*, increasing a woman's chances of becoming
       pregnant after intercourse *[1 mark]*.
  c) i) in vitro fertilisation/IVF *[1 mark]*
    ii) To stimulate egg production/allow multiple eggs to be collected
       [1 mark].
3 a)   A high level of oestrogen inhibits FSH production *[1 mark]*,
       which causes egg production and development to stop *[1 mark]*.
  b)   E.g. hormonal methods are generally more effective at
       preventing pregnancy than barrier methods when used correctly
       [1 mark]. Hormonal methods mean the couple don't have to
       think about contraception each time they have intercourse, unlike
       with barrier methods *[1 mark]*.
4 a) i) Progesterone inhibits the release of FSH *[1 mark]* and LH
       [1 mark], which stimulate egg maturation and ovulation
       [1 mark].
    ii) E.g. it stimulates the production of thick cervical mucus
       [1 mark], which prevents sperm from entering the uterus and
       reaching an egg *[1 mark]*.
  b)   So they are protected against sexually transmitted infections/
       STIs *[1 mark]*.
  c)   E.g. she doesn't need to remember to take a pill (at the same
       time) every day *[1 mark]*.

Page 84 — Homeostasis — Control of Blood Glucose

1 a)   It means maintaining a constant internal environment *[1 mark]*.
  b)   pancreas *[1 mark]*
2 a)   The blood glucose concentration starts increasing as glucose
       from the drink is absorbed into the blood *[1 mark]*.
       The pancreas detects a high blood glucose concentration and
       secretes insulin *[1 mark]*. Insulin causes the blood glucose
       concentration to fall back to normal *[1 mark]*.

Topic 8

b) i) glucagon *[1 mark]*

ii) It increases the concentration of glucose in the blood *[1 mark]* because it causes glycogen stores in the liver and muscles *[1 mark]* to be converted into glucose, which is released into the blood *[1 mark]*.

Page 85 — Diabetes

1 a) i) So he can calculate the patient's BMI *[1 mark]*, as obesity/a BMI above 30 is associated with an increased risk of developing type 2 diabetes *[1 mark]*.

ii) Her waist circumference and hip circumference *[1 mark]*. These measurements will allow him to calculate the patient's waist-to-hip ratio *[1 mark]*, as a high waist-to-hip ratio/abdominal obesity is associated with an increased risk of developing type 2 diabetes *[1 mark]*.

b) Any two from: e.g. eat a healthy diet / get regular exercise / lose weight (if necessary) / take medication/insulin injections *[2 marks — 1 mark for each correct answer]*

c) The pancreas doesn't produce enough insulin *[1 mark]*. A person becomes resistant to insulin *[1 mark]*.

2 a) i) The pancreas of a person with type 1 diabetes produces little or no insulin *[1 mark]*, so a pancreas transplant would provide the person with a permanent new source of insulin *[1 mark]*.

ii) E.g. a pancreas transplant is a serious operation, which carries the risk of complications *[1 mark]*. / There aren't enough donor pancreases available *[1 mark]*. / Drugs need to be taken afterwards to suppress the immune system *[1 mark]*.

You're not expected to know the answer to this question, you're just expected to make a sensible suggestion.

b) E.g. regular insulin injections/insulin therapy *[1 mark]*.

Page 86 — Thermoregulation

1 a) D *[1 mark]*

37 °C is the optimum temperature for enzymes in the human body — above this temperature they may start to denature and below this temperature they slow down.

b) temperature of the blood *[1 mark]*

c) The skin contains temperature receptors *[1 mark]*. These send nervous impulses to the thermoregulatory centre *[1 mark]*.

2 a) i) Dermis — Contains sweat glands which produce sweat *[1 mark]* Epidermis — Contains pores to release the sweat (onto the surface of the skin) *[1 mark]*.

ii) When sweat evaporates from the surface of the skin *[1 mark]* it transfers energy to the environment, which cools the body down *[1 mark]*.

b) Vasoconstriction — Less blood flows near the surface of the skin *[1 mark]*, so less energy is transferred to the environment *[1 mark]*, which helps to keep the body warm *[1 mark]*. Shivering — Muscles contract automatically *[1 mark]*. This increases the rate of respiration *[1 mark]*, which transfers more energy to warm the body *[1 mark]*.

Pages 87-88 — Osmoregulation and The Kidneys

Warm-up
water, cells, osmosis, kidneys

1 a) A — glomerulus *[1 mark]*, B — Bowman's capsule *[1 mark]*

b) Sufficient amounts of them are reabsorbed into the blood *[1 mark]*.

c) C *[1 mark]*

When glucose moves from the nephron back into the blood it moves against its concentration gradient, so it's not moved by diffusion. Osmosis only involves the movement of water molecules and filtration is the process by which molecules are squeezed out of the blood into the nephron.

d) It is produced in the liver from the breakdown of excess amino acids *[1 mark]*.

e) Urine leaves the nephrons via the collecting ducts *[1 mark]* and passes into the ureter *[1 mark]*. It then passes into the bladder *[1 mark]* before leaving the body via the urethra *[1 mark]*.

2 If the water concentration of the blood became too high then water would move into the cells by osmosis *[1 mark]*, which could cause the cells to burst *[1 mark]*. If the water concentration of the blood became too low then water would move out of the cells by osmosis *[1 mark]*, which could cause the cells to shrink *[1 mark]*.

3 a) Amount of glucose reabsorbed = 100 % *[1 mark]*

Remember, in a healthy person all the glucose that enters the nephron is selectively reabsorbed back into the blood.

b) Proteins are too big to be filtered from the blood *[1 mark]*.

c)

Concentration of the substance is the **same** in the renal vein as it is in the renal artery.	Concentration of the substance is **lower** in the renal vein than it is in the renal artery.
Glucose Protein	Water Sodium

[2 marks — 1 mark for each column completed correctly]

The first thing you need to understand in this question is that the renal artery is the blood vessel that supplies the kidney with blood and the renal vein is the blood vessel in which blood leaves the kidney. As all of the glucose is reabsorbed in the kidney, the glucose concentration of the blood will be the same when it leaves the kidney as it was when it entered. It's a similar story for protein — as none is filtered from the blood in the first place, its concentration doesn't differ between the renal artery and the renal vein. Not all of the water and sodium that enters the kidney in the renal artery is reabsorbed, so the concentration of these two substances will be lower in the renal vein than in the renal artery.

d) Percentage of water not reabsorbed = $100 - 99.2 = 0.8\%$
So amount of water lost in urine = 0.8% of 180 dm³
$= (180 \div 100) \times 0.8 = \textbf{1.44 dm}^3 \textbf{ day}^{-1}$
[3 marks for correct answer, otherwise 1 mark for 100 – 99.2 and 1 mark for 0.8% of 180 dm³]

Or: Percentage of water reabsorbed = 99.2% of 180 dm³
$= (180 \div 100) \times 99.2 = 178.56 \text{ dm}^3 \text{ day}^{-1}$
So amount of water lost in urine =
$180 - 178.56 = \textbf{1.44 dm}^3 \textbf{ day}^{-1}$
[3 marks for correct answer, otherwise 1 mark for 99.2% of 180 dm³ and 1 mark for 180 – 178.56]

Page 89 — More on The Kidneys

Warm-up
pituitary, more, more, water

1 a) Waste substances, excess ions and excess water *[1 mark]* are filtered out of the blood *[1 mark]*.

b) So that useful substances won't be lost from the person's blood during dialysis *[1 mark]*.

c) i) kidney transplant *[1 mark]*

ii) E.g. they may have to wait a long time for a kidney donor with a tissue type that closely matches their own *[1 mark]*.

2 If not enough ADH is produced then the collecting ducts will be less permeable to water *[1 mark]* and not enough water will be reabsorbed from the kidneys into the blood *[1 mark]*. This will mean that the water content of the blood falls *[1 mark]*, so the person will need to drink more water to maintain the water content of the blood *[1 mark]*.

Topic 8 — Exchange and Transport in Animals

Page 90 — Exchange of Materials

1 a) Any two from: e.g. oxygen / mineral ions / water / dissolved food molecules. *[2 marks — 1 mark for each correct answer]*

b) Sticklebacks are multicellular *[1 mark]* so they can't simply exchange all the substances they need across the outer surface of their body *[1 mark]*. They need specialised exchange surfaces for efficient diffusion of substances into and out of their body *[1 mark]* and a mass transport system to carry substances around their body *[1 mark]*.

Topic 8

2 a)   X = (3 × 3) × 6 = **54 cm²** *[1 mark]*
            Y = 3 × 3 × 3 = **27 cm³** *[1 mark]*
            Z = 150 ÷ 125 = **1.2** *[1 mark]*
  b)   5 × 5 × 5, because it has the smallest surface area to volume ratio *[1 mark]*.

As this cube had the smallest surface area in relation to its volume, it would take the acid longest to diffuse throughout this cube and change its colour.

Pages 91-92 — Diffusion and the Alveoli

1 a)

$$\text{Rate of diffusion} \propto \frac{\text{surface area} \times \textbf{concentration difference}}{\textbf{thickness of membrane}}$$

     [2 marks — 1 mark for each correct variable in the correct position.]
  b)   The rate of diffusion would double *[1 mark]*.

Remember that 'α' means 'proportional to' — whatever happens to one side of the 'proportional to' sign will also happen to the other side. So if you double the surface area of the cell, that's the same as multiplying the right hand side by 2. So the rate of diffusion will also be multiplied by 2 (i.e. doubled).

2 a)   Increasing the concentration of ammonia increases the rate of diffusion *[1 mark]*.
  b)   E.g. the surface area of the cell *[1 mark]*, the distance for diffusion *[1 mark]*.
  c)   E.g. by repeating the experiment and calculating a mean *[1 mark]*.
3 a)   A — carbon dioxide *[1 mark]*, B — oxygen *[1 mark]*
  b)   Blood flowing past the alveolus has a lower concentration of oxygen than in the alveolus *[1 mark]* and a higher concentration of carbon dioxide than in the alveolus *[1 mark]*. This means there's a high concentration gradient for both gases so the rate of diffusion is high *[1 mark]*.
  c)   Any two from: e.g. they have a moist lining *[1 mark]* to allow gases to dissolve *[1 mark]*. / The walls of the alveoli are very thin *[1 mark]* to minimise the distance that the gases must diffuse across *[1 mark]*. / There are many alveoli in the lungs *[1 mark]* to maximise the total surface area over which gas exchange takes place *[1 mark]*.
4   As there are fewer alveoli in the lungs, the amount of surface area in the lungs is reduced *[1 mark]*, so the amount of oxygen that can diffuse into the blood (from the air spaces in the alveoli) at any one time is reduced *[1 mark]*. This means that a person with emphysema absorbs less oxygen in each breath, and so may have to breathe more rapidly to deliver enough oxygen to their body cells *[1 mark]*.

Page 93 — Circulatory System — Blood

1 a)   B *[1 mark]*
  b)   white blood cells / lymphocytes *[1 mark]*
  c)   It is a liquid *[1 mark]* that transports many different substances in the blood *[1 mark]*.
2 a)   plasma *[1 mark]*
  b)   Red blood cells carry oxygen around the body *[1 mark]*. A biconcave shape increases the surface area to allow a greater absorption of oxygen *[1 mark]*.
  c)   Platelets are involved in helping blood to clot at a wound *[1 mark]*. Therefore, a low level of platelets may lead to excessive bleeding/bruising / an inability to form blood clots *[1 mark]*.

Page 94 — Circulatory System — Blood Vessels

Warm-up
A — artery, B — vein, C — capillary
1 a) i)   veins *[1 mark]*
    ii)   To ensure that blood keeps flowing in the right direction *[1 mark]*.
  b)   capillaries *[1 mark]*

2 a)   Arteries have a thicker layer of smooth muscle compared to veins *[1 mark]*. Arteries transport blood away from the heart *[1 mark]* so the blood is at a greater pressure than the blood carried in veins *[1 mark]*. The thicker layer of muscle in arteries makes them stronger to withstand this pressure *[1 mark]*.
  b)   Being narrow allows capillaries to squeeze into the gaps between cells *[1 mark]* so they can exchange substances with every cell *[1 mark]*.

Pages 95-96 — Circulatory System — Heart

Warm-up
Deoxygenated, vena cava, right ventricle, artery, lungs, valve
1 a)   X: aorta *[1 mark]*, Y: pulmonary vein *[1 mark]*, Z: left atrium *[1 mark]*
  b)

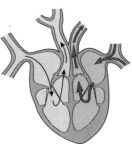

     [1 mark for arrow(s) showing blood flow from the vena cava, through the right atrium and ventricle, then up through the pulmonary artery.]
2   The wall of the left ventricle is thicker than the wall of the right ventricle *[1 mark]*. This is because the left ventricle needs to be stronger than the right ventricle *[1 mark]* because it pumps blood around the whole body, whereas the right ventricle only pumps blood to the lungs *[1 mark]*.
3 a)   The volume of blood pumped by one ventricle each time it contracts *[1 mark]*.
  b)   cardiac output = heart rate × stroke volume
         57 × 84 = **4788 cm³ min⁻¹** *[2 marks for correct answer, otherwise 1 mark for 57 × 84.]*
  c)   heart rate = cardiac output ÷ stroke volume
         4095 ÷ 65 = **63 bpm** *[2 marks for correct answer, otherwise 1 mark for 4095 ÷ 65.]*
  d)   The ventricles of a larger heart are likely to have a greater volume than those in a smaller heart *[1 mark]*. This means that a person with a larger heart is likely to have a greater stroke volume than a person with a smaller heart *[1 mark]*. A greater stroke volume is likely to mean a greater cardiac output *[1 mark]*.
  e)   The increase in heart rate will lead to an increased cardiac output *[1 mark]*.

Pages 97-98 — Respiration

1 a)   A *[1 mark]*
  b)   They result in the transfer of energy from glucose/food *[1 mark]*, which is used for important metabolic processes *[1 mark]*.
  c) i)   E.g. glucose *[1 mark]*
    ii)   oxygen *[1 mark]*
    iii)   carbon dioxide *[1 mark]* and water *[1 mark]*
  d)   Aerobic respiration is more efficient / transfers more energy compared to anaerobic respiration *[1 mark]*. / Unlike anaerobic respiration, aerobic doesn't produce lactic acid, which can be painful *[1 mark]*.
  e)   E.g. during vigorous exercise *[1 mark]*.
  f)   In plants the products of anaerobic respiration are ethanol *[1 mark]* and carbon dioxide *[1 mark]*, whereas in animals the only product is lactic acid *[1 mark]*.
2 a)   The percentage of oxygen in exhaled air is less than in inhaled air because oxygen has been used by the body in aerobic respiration *[1 mark]*.

b) There will be a greater percentage of carbon dioxide in exhaled air than in inhaled air *[1 mark]* because carbon dioxide is produced in the body by aerobic respiration *[1 mark]*.
Remember that carbon dioxide (a waste product of respiration) diffuses from the blood to the air in the alveoli in the lungs, which is then breathed out.
3 a) Oxygen consumption increased rapidly at first then more slowly *[1 mark]*, until around 8 minutes when it levelled off *[1 mark]*.
b) In the final two minutes of exercise, the man's oxygen consumption remained constant *[1 mark]*. This suggests that his muscles were respiring anaerobically to supply the extra energy needed for his muscles to continue to work harder, as this process doesn't require oxygen *[1 mark]*.

Page 99 — Investigating Respiration
1 a) E.g. the snail must have enough oxygen for two hours / the snail must not dry out *[1 mark]*.
b) The glass beads are acting as a control *[1 mark]* to show that any change in the carbon dioxide concentration of Beaker A is due to the snail and not some other factor *[1 mark]*.
c) The percentage of carbon dioxide in the air has increased over the two hours because the snail releases carbon dioxide as it respires *[1 mark]*.
d) It would have decreased *[1 mark]* because the snail would have used up oxygen as it respired *[1 mark]*.
e) The internal temperature of Beaker A would be higher than that of Beaker B / the internal temperature of Beaker A would increase whereas the internal temperature of Beaker B would stay the same *[1 mark]* because during respiration energy is transferred to the environment by heat *[1 mark]*.

Topic 9 — Ecosystems and Material Cycles

Pages 100-101 — Ecosystems & Interactions Between Organisms
Warm-up

Abiotic	Biotic
pollutants temperature light intensity water	prey species predators competition

1 a) B *[1 mark]*
b) A community of organisms and the abiotic conditions in which they live *[1 mark]*.
2 a) E.g. the number of birds in the grassland may decrease *[1 mark]*, as the new predator would compete with the birds over the insects *[1 mark]*.
b) E.g. it may decrease *[1 mark]*. With fewer birds to eat the insects, insect numbers may increase *[1 mark]*. More insects would eat more grass, reducing grass plant numbers *[1 mark]*.
3 a) Parasitism *[1 mark]* because the cuckoo benefits from the relationship but the host does not *[1 mark]*.
b) B *[1 mark]*
The information given in the question describes benefits for both the ants and the trees. This is what makes it a mutualistic relationship.
4 a) E.g. it may have increased *[1 mark]* because prickly acacia grow best when there is plenty of water *[1 mark]*.
b) E.g. the prickly acacia may become distributed over a wider area *[1 mark]*, as they may spread into areas that were previously too cold for them *[1 mark]*.
c) E.g. the prickly acacia may compete with the grasses for resources (such as light, water, space and nutrients) *[1 mark]* causing their populations to decrease *[1 mark]*.

Pages 102-103 — Investigating Ecosystems
1 a) i) To avoid any bias in the sampling *[1 mark]*.
ii) E.g. divide the field into a grid and place the quadrats at coordinates selected using a random number generator *[1 mark]*.
b) 13 buttercups *[1 mark]*
Remember that the mode is the most frequently occurring number.

c) 15.5 buttercups *[1 mark]*
To answer this question, simply put the numbers of buttercups in each quadrat in order from the smallest to the largest, like this: 12, 13, 13, 13, 15, 16, 16, 23, 23, 26. The median number is halfway along this list — so it lies halfway between 15 and 16.
d) 15 + 13 + 16 + 23 + 26 + 23 + 13 + 12 + 16 + 13 = 170
170 ÷ 10 = **17 buttercups per 0.5 m²** *[1 mark]*
e) 17 × 2 = 34 per m²
34 × 1750 = **59 500 buttercups** *[2 marks for the correct answer, otherwise 1 mark for multiplying answer to part d) by 2.]*
2 a) Zone B and Zone C *[1 mark]*
b) long grass *[1 mark]*
c) Zone A is closest to the pond where the soil has more moisture *[1 mark]*. Zone A also has the highest light intensity *[1 mark]*.
d) Zone B *[1 mark]* because only short grass grows here *[1 mark]*.
e) E.g. the light level may be too low *[1 mark]*. / They are unable to compete with the trees for resources, e.g. water *[1 mark]*.

Pages 104-105 — Ecosystems and Energy Transfers
Warm-up
biomass, the Sun, animals, lost, trophic level
1 a)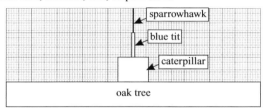
[1 mark for pyramid with all four trophic levels shown in the correct order. 1 mark for all four trophic levels plotted correctly to scale.]
b) The biomass decreases as the trophic level increases *[1 mark]*, so there's not enough energy/biomass to support more trophic levels *[1 mark]*.
2 a) 4000 ÷ 50 000 = 0.08
0.08 × 100 = **8%** *[2 marks for correct answer or 1 mark for 4000 ÷ 50 000]*
b) 8 + 9 + 10 = 27
27 ÷ 3 = **9%** *[1 mark for correct answer or for (answer to part a + 9 + 10) ÷ 3]*
c) The efficiency of energy transfer is so low because a lot of energy is 'lost' at each trophic level and is not transferred to the next level up *[1 mark]*. Some of this 'lost' energy is transferred to the surroundings by heat during respiration *[1 mark]*. Some of this energy is 'lost' because not all parts of an organism (e.g. bones) get eaten *[1 mark]* and because not all parts that do get eaten can be digested *[1 mark]*.

Page 106 — Human Impacts on Biodiversity
1 Any two from: e.g. they may have out-competed native species for resources/food/shelter *[1 mark]*. / They may have brought new diseases to New Zealand, which infected/killed large numbers of native species *[1 mark]*. / They may have fed/preyed on native species *[1 mark]*.
2 a) How to grade your answer:
Level 0: There is no relevant information. *[0 marks]*
Level 1: There is some information about how the application of fertilisers on farmland may reduce the biodiversity of nearby water sources. The points made are basic and not linked together. *[1-2 marks]*
Level 2: There is some explanation of how the application of fertilisers on farmland may reduce the biodiversity of nearby water sources. Some of the points made are linked together. *[3-4 marks]*
Level 3: There is a clear and detailed explanation of how the application of fertilisers on farmland may reduce the biodiversity of nearby water sources. The points made are well-linked and the answer has a clear and logical structure. *[5-6 marks]*

Here are some points your answer may include:
Many fertilisers contain nitrates. If too much fertiliser is applied to the fields, it will run off the fields when it rains into nearby water sources, leading to eutrophication. This is where excess nitrates in the water cause algae to grow fast and block out light. This means that less light reaches plants, which then can't photosynthesise and so die. The microorganisms that feed on dead plants increase in number and use up the oxygen in the water. This means that there is not enough oxygen available for other organisms, e.g. fish, which then also die. The death of all of these organisms reduces biodiversity.

b) E.g. the food given to the fish/the waste produced by the fish leaks out into the surrounding water and increases the nutrient content of the water *[1 mark]*. This leads to eutrophication in the same way fertilisers in the water do *[1 mark]*.

c) Any two from: e.g. other species may swim into the nets and become trapped and die, reducing the number of species and therefore biodiversity in the water *[1 mark]*. / Farmed fish may escape into the wild and cause the death of indigenous species, leading to a reduction in biodiversity *[1 mark]*. / The fish farms may acts as a breeding ground for parasites which could get out and infect and kill wild populations of fish, reducing biodiversity *[1 mark]*.

Page 107 — Conservation and Biodiversity

1 a) If one species goes extinct then the food chain that it is a part of will be disrupted *[1 mark]*. Protecting one species, will help to protect the species that feed on it *[1 mark]*. / Efforts to protect one species may involve the protection of the habitat of that species *[1 mark]*, in which case, other species within that habitat will also be protected *[1 mark]*.

b) E.g. the species may attract ecotourism which brings money to a country. / The protection of the species may lead to the creation of jobs *[1 mark]*.

Make sure you read the question carefully here — whatever you write down must be relevant to helping the economy of the country in some way.

2 How to grade your answer:
Level 0: There is no relevant information. *[0 marks]*
Level 1: There is some information about the possible benefits of reforestation for biodiversity or local farmers or Ethiopian society. The points made are basic and not linked together. *[1-2 marks]*
Level 2: There is some discussion of the possible benefits of reforestation for at least two of biodiversity, local farmers and Ethiopian society. Some of the points made are linked together. *[3-4 marks]*
Level 3: There is a clear and detailed discussion of the possible benefits of reforestation for biodiversity, local farmers and Ethiopian society. The points made are well-linked and the answer has a clear and logical structure. *[5-6 marks]*
Here are some points your answer may include:
By reforesting the land, the soil will be less exposed to the rain and Sun, so there will be less soil erosion and drought. This will help to increase soil quality and make it easier for farmers to grow crops on the land. This in turn will mean that there will be more food available for the rest of the Ethiopian population. Increased forest cover is also likely to increase the biodiversity of the area, as many more species will be able to survive in the forested areas. Increased biodiversity may bring more money to Ethiopia through ecotourism, which will help to benefit Ethiopian society. Ecotourism and the reforestation programmes themselves will create new jobs, so more people will have an income. Reforestation may also help to protect species that are important to Ethiopia's cultural heritage, or plants that could be beneficial as medicines.

Page 108 — Food Security

1 a) Meeting the needs of today's population without affecting the ability of future generations to meet their needs *[1 mark]*.

b) E.g. overfishing wild fish may mean that there aren't enough fish available to catch in the future *[1 mark]*.

c) Growing biofuels takes up land that could be used for food crops *[1 mark]*.

2 a) The increasing temperature may reduce crop growth / lead to other forms of climate change (e.g. changing rainfall patterns) that reduce crop growth *[1 mark]*. This may reduce crop yields *[1 mark]*, which may mean we are unable to grow enough (safe, nutritious) food to feed the growing human population *[1 mark]*.

b) The resistant pests will not be killed by the pesticides and will damage crops *[1 mark]*, leading to lower yields and less food produced *[1 mark]*.

c) An increased amount of animal farming would reduce food security *[1 mark]*. This is because, for a given area of land, less food is produced by rearing livestock than growing crops *[1 mark]* and because livestock must be fed crops that could be given directly to humans *[1 mark]*.

Page 109 — The Carbon Cycle

1 a) i) photosynthesis *[1 mark]*
   ii) Process A / photosynthesis converts carbon dioxide from the air into carbon compounds in plants, making carbon available for use in the ecosystem *[1 mark]*.
b) burning/combustion *[1 mark]*
c) Carbon dioxide is returned back to the atmosphere *[1 mark]* when the microorganisms involved in decay respire *[1 mark]*.
d) Biotic: e.g. animals / plants / microorganisms *[1 mark]*
   Abiotic: e.g. fossil fuels / air *[1 mark]*

Page 110 — The Water Cycle

Warm-up
evaporate, water vapour, cools, precipitation
1 a) B *[1 mark]*
b) The concentration of salt in sea water is too high *[1 mark]*.
2 E.g. by boiling sea water in a vessel *[1 mark]* so that the water evaporates to form steam and leaves the salt behind *[1 mark]*. The steam then enters a pipe connected to the vessel, where it condenses *[1 mark]* back into pure water, which can be collected for drinking *[1 mark]*. / Sea water may be fed into a vessel with a partially permeable membrane at a high pressure *[1 mark]*. The high pressure will cause the water molecules to move in the reverse direction to osmosis/from a higher salt concentration to a lower salt concentration *[1 mark]*. The water is forced through the membrane, leaving the salt behind *[1 mark]* and allowing pure water to be collected for drinking *[1 mark]*.

Pages 111-112 — The Nitrogen Cycle

1 a) E.g. to make proteins *[1 mark]*
b) B *[1 mark]*
2 a) i) C *[1 mark]*
   ii) D *[1 mark]* and E *[1 mark]*
   iii) A *[1 mark]* and B *[1 mark]*
b) D *[1 mark]*
c) Decomposers break down proteins in dead plants and animals/ urea *[1 mark]* and turn it into ammonia *[1 mark]*.
3 a) There are lots of nitrogen-containing compounds in the soil in the new plot *[1 mark]* because the pea plants/legumes that were previously grown in the plot contained nitrogen-fixing bacteria in their root nodules *[1 mark]*. This means that the cabbages were able to obtain more nitrogen in the new plot and no longer showed any nitrogen deficiency symptoms *[1 mark]*.
b) To add nitrogen-containing compounds back into the soil which the vegetable plants need for growth *[1 mark]*.
c) Wet soils will mean that denitrifying bacteria are more active, and so more nitrates in the soil will be turned back into nitrogen gas *[1 mark]*, which plants can't use directly *[1 mark]*. This means less nitrogen will be available to the cabbages and they may start to show deficiency symptoms again *[1 mark]*.

Mixed Questions

Page 113 — Indicator Species

1 a) E.g. bloodworm *[1 mark]*, sludgeworm *[1 mark]*
   b) That the level of pollution is low *[1 mark]* because stonefly prefer clean water *[1 mark]*.
2 a) The further away from the road the greater the number of lichen species *[1 mark]*, because the concentration of sulfur dioxide from cars gets lower further from the road *[1 mark]*.
   b) 25 m *[1 mark]*
   c) E.g. factors other than pollution may contribute to the presence or absence of the indicator species *[1 mark]*. You can't use indicator species to measure exactly how polluted an area is *[1 mark]*.

Pages 114-115 — Decomposition

Warm-up

True, True, True, False

1 E.g. food can be dried *[1 mark]*. This limits the amount of water available for the microorganisms involved in decay to use in biological processes *[1 mark]*. / Food can be refrigerated *[1 mark]*. This slows the rate of reproduction of microorganisms involved in decay *[1 mark]*. / Salt or sugar can be added to food *[1 mark]*. This causes the microorganisms involved in decay to lose water by osmosis, killing them *[1 mark]*.
2 a) E.g. mesh sides increase oxygen availability *[1 mark]* for the aerobic respiration of microorganisms involved in decomposition *[1 mark]*.
   b) The microorganisms involved in decomposition need water in order to survive and carry out biological processes *[1 mark]*.
   c) The rate of decomposition will increase *[1 mark]* because the increasing temperature will increase the rate of enzyme-controlled reactions in the microorganisms involved in decay *[1 mark]*.
3 a)

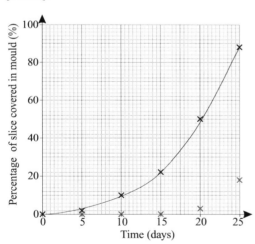

   [2 marks for all six points plotted correctly, otherwise 1 mark for 4 points plotted correctly. 1 mark for the points being joined by a smooth curve of best fit, which goes through or as close to as many points as possible.]
   b) Days 20 and 25 *[1 mark]*
   c) 88% − 22% = 66%
      25 days − 15 days = 10 days
      66 ÷ 10 = **6.6 % day⁻¹** *[2 marks for the correct answer or 1 mark for dividing the percentage change by 10.]*
   d) 18% − 3% = 15%
      15 ÷ 5 = 3% day⁻¹
      3 ÷ 24 = 0.125 = **0.13% hour⁻¹**
      [3 marks for the correct answer, otherwise 1 mark for 15% and 1 mark for the correct calculation of rate.]
   e) Any two from: e.g. amount of water used to moisten slices / type of bread used / age of bread used / size of slice / humidity of room and refrigerator *[1 mark for each]*.

Mixed Questions

Pages 116-124 — Mixed Questions

1 a) i) mitochondria *[1 mark]*
      ii) oxygen *[1 mark]*, carbon dioxide *[1 mark]*
   b) plasma *[1 mark]*
   c) Glucagon is released into the blood *[1 mark]*, which converts glycogen back into glucose *[1 mark]*.
2 a) producer *[1 mark]*
   b)

   | stoats |
   | blue tits |
   | greenflies |
   | green plants | *[1 mark]*

   Don't forget, the producer always goes on the bottom of a pyramid of biomass, then the next trophic level goes on top of that and so on.
   c) Biotic: e.g. increased competition / increase in greenfly numbers *[1 mark]*.
      Abiotic: e.g. a change in light intensity / pollution / water availability / temperature *[1 mark]*.

   Remember, biotic factors are 'living' factors that affect an environment, and abiotic factors are 'non-living' factors.
3 a) i) B *[1 mark]*
      ii) urea *[1 mark]*
   b) A *[1 mark]*
   c) i) 40 °C *[1 mark]*
      ii) The enzyme will not work *[1 mark]* because the high temperature will change the shape of its active site/denature the enzyme *[1 mark]* and the substrate will no longer fit *[1 mark]*.
4 a) RR *[1 mark]*
   b) round seed shape *[1 mark]*
   c)

	R	R
r	Rr	Rr
r	Rr	Rr

   [1 mark]
   The parents' genotypes were RR and rr *[1 mark]*.
5 a) i) Take several small pieces of tissue from fast growing regions/ the root tips/the shoot tips of the parent plant *[1 mark]*. Grow the tissue in a growth medium containing nutrients and growth hormones *[1 mark]*. As the tissues produce shoots and roots move them to potting compost to carry on growing into full plants *[1 mark]*.
      ii) E.g. tissue culture is faster. / Tissue culture requires less space. / Tissue culture can be carried out at any time of year. / Tissue culture produces clones/genetically identical plants. *[1 mark]*
   b) i) 5 mm = 0.5 cm
      area = πr^2 = 3.14 × 0.5² = **0.8 cm²** *[3 marks for correct answer, otherwise 1 mark for 0.5 cm and 1 mark for area = πr^2]*
      ii)

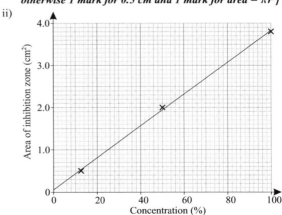

   [1 mark for axes with suitable scale and labelled correctly, 1 mark for all points plotted correctly, 1 mark for a suitable straight line of best fit.]

Answers

Mixed Questions

iii) 3.1 cm² *[1 mark. Accept answers between 3.0 and 3.2 cm².]*

iv) The higher the concentration of the plant extract, the more effective it is at preventing bacterial growth *[1 mark]*.

6 a) The hormone is secreted directly into the blood *[1 mark]*. It is then carried in the blood to the target organ *[1 mark]*.

b) It inhibits the secretion of both FSH *[1 mark]* and LH *[1 mark]*.

c) i) C *[1 mark]*

ii) B *[1 mark]*

d) oestrogen *[1 mark]*, progesterone *[1 mark]*

e) It causes an egg to mature in one of the ovaries *[1 mark]*. It stimulates the ovaries to produce oestrogen *[1 mark]*.

7 a) A non-communicable disease because it is not transmitted between individuals/is not caused by a pathogen *[1 mark]*.

Remember, communicable diseases are caused by pathogens and can be spread between individuals. Vitamin A deficiency is caused by deficiencies in the diet, so it's non-communicable.

b) It will contain genes not found in normal rice / DNA from a bacterium and a maize plant *[1 mark]*.

c) E.g. the genes to be used from the maize plant and the soil bacterium were cut out using restriction enzymes *[1 mark]*. The same restriction enzymes were used to cut open the DNA of a vector *[1 mark]*. The genes extracted from the maize plant and the soil bacterium were then joined to the vector DNA using ligase enzymes *[1 mark]*. The recombinant DNA/vector containing the desired genes were then have been inserted into a rice plant to produce Golden Rice *[1 mark]*.

d) Any two from: e.g. the rice could have adverse affects on human health that aren't yet known. / Growing Golden Rice doesn't tackle the underlying cause of poor diet in many developing countries, which is poverty. / Countries may become dependant on companies who sell seeds for Golden Rice. / Money/resources may be wasted planting Golden Rice seeds in areas where environmental factors (e.g. soil quality) will prevent it from growing well. *[2 marks]*

8 a) i) There is less variation (in tomato size) in Generation X than in Generation A *[1 mark]*. This is because selective breeding has led to a smaller gene pool/a smaller variety of alleles in Generation X than in Generation A *[1 mark]*.

ii) 17.1 – 12.7 = 4.4 cm
(4.4 ÷ 12.7) × 100 = **34.6%**
[2 marks for correct answer, otherwise 1 mark for correct working.]

To calculate percentage change, you first need to work out the difference between the two figures. You then need calculate what percentage that difference is of the first figure.

b) Plants make proteins using nitrogen *[1 mark]* from nitrates/nitrogen ions in the fertiliser *[1 mark]*.

9 a) i) oxygen *[1 mark]*

ii) light intensity *[1 mark]*

The foil prevents any light from reaching the algae.

iii) Tube 1 shows that in the dark, the algae are producing more carbon dioxide than they take in *[1 mark]*. The concentration of carbon dioxide is high because the cells are respiring, but not photosynthesising (as there's no light for photosynthesis to take place) *[1 mark]*. Tube 2 shows that in the light, the algae are taking up more carbon dioxide than they produce *[1 mark]*. The concentration of carbon dioxide has reduced because the cells are photosynthesising faster than they are respiring *[1 mark]*.

Plant cells respire all the time but they can only photosynthesise when it's light.

iv) Any two from: e.g. the temperature of the boiling tubes / the volume of hydrogencarbonate indicator / the concentration of hydrogencarbonate indicator / the number of beads in each tube / the concentration of algal cells in each bead *[2 marks — 1 mark for each correct answer]*.

b) i) Light intensity *[1 mark]* because the rate of photosynthesis is increasing as the light intensity increases *[1 mark]*.

ii) carbon dioxide concentration *[1 mark]*

10 a) E.g. using mosquito nets / insect repellant (to prevent biting) *[1 mark]*.

b) mitosis *[1 mark]*

c) There are fewer red blood cells to carry oxygen to all the cells in the body *[1 mark]*. This means that the cells aren't receiving enough oxygen for respiration/transferring energy from glucose *[1 mark]*.

d) i) E.g. a flushing agent is used to help the blood sample flow from one end of the stick to the other through the paper strip *[1 mark]*.

ii) Antibodies complementary to the malaria antigen are stuck to the strip at point B *[1 mark]*. Malaria antigens bound to the dye-labelled antibodies have flowed along the strip from point A to point B *[1 mark]* where they have bound to antibodies that are stuck to the strip *[1 mark]*. Because the antibodies containing dye have bound at point B they are visible there as a coloured line *[1 mark]*.

ISBN 978 1 78294 500 0

9 781782 945000

BEQA41   £2.00
              (Retail Price)

www.cgpbooks.co.uk